Proficiency
Masterclass

Workbook
With Answers

Proficiency

Masterclass

Workbook
With Answers

Kathy Gude

Michael Duckworth

OXFORD UNIVERSITY PRESS 1998

Acknowledgements

The authors and publisher are grateful to those who have given permission to reproduce the following extracts and adaptations of copyright material:

p9 'It's a Dog's Life' by Brigit Grant, with permission of John Brown Publishing Ltd; p16 'The Big Bang' by Charlie Rushmore, with permission of John Brown Publishing Ltd; p19 'The Twilight Zone' by Jim Horne © The Guardian; p22 'Meet the Dream Detectives' by Robin Cross, with permission of John Brown Publishing Ltd; p24 extract from A Mind to Crime: The Controversial Link Between the Mind and Criminal Behaviour by Anne Moir and David Jessel, Michael Joseph (1995) © Anne Moir and David Jessel, 1995 reproduced by permission of Penguin Books; p26 'Have Fridge, Will Travel', article and photograph, by permission of Stephen Bates, Staff Correspondent with The Guardian; p32 extract from Sister Wendy's Grand Tour published by BBC Books © Sister Wendy Beckett 1994; p36 & p40 extract from Bad Land by Jonathan Raban by permission of Picador; p41 'Analysing Handwriting' in The Cambridge Encyclopedia of Language by D. Crystal, 1995, by permission of Cambridge University Press; p41 extract from A Manual of Graphology by Eric Singer, by permission of Gerald Duckworth and Company Ltd; p47 & p49 'Whose Wildlife is it Anyway?' by David Stirling by permission of Save The Rhino International; p56 from THE TOTAL PACKAGE by Thomas Hine © 1995 by Thomas Hine, by permission of Little, Brown and Company (Inc.); p59 extract from More Power To You! by Connie Brown Glaser & Barbara Steinberg Smalley, Century Business Books; p62 extract from 'Old Wives' Tales' from Collected Short Stories by Ruth Rendell reprinted by permission of the Peters Fraser & Dunlop Group Ltd; p64 extract from The Serpent and the Mousetrap by Professor John Wren-Lewis with his permission; p66 'Sweat, Sawdust and Surrealism' by Jon Wilde with permission of John Brown Publishing Ltd; p76 'Today Was Gonna Be The Day' © The Guardian; p77 'The Hero Who Saved New Year' by Sarah O'Grady with permission of The Express; p78 'Parachutists Fall 1,600 feet and Survive' with permission of The Express.

Although every effort has been made to trace and contact copyright holders before publication, this has not always been possible. We apologize for any apparent infringement of copyright and if notified, the publisher will be pleased to rectify any errors or omissions at the earliest opportunity.

Illustrations by:
Mark Aston pp33, 40, 58, 79; Stephan Chabluk p56; Emma Dodd p78; David Eaton p24; Nigel Paige pp18, 44, 48; Stephen Player/Artist Partners p66; Willie Ryan p8; Axel Scheffler pp7, 42, 51; Harry Venning pp10, 14, 15, 20, 25, 28, 35, 39, 45, 49, 51, 60, 64, 70, 74, 80; Michael Woods p46.

Handwriting by:
Kathy Baxendale pp34, 55.

The publishers would like to thank the following for permission to reproduce photographs:
Bridgeman Art Library p32; Jonathan Cape/Jerry Bauer p14; Cherwell Valley Services/ Richard Oliver p19; Bruce Coleman/Christer Fredriksson p50; Getty Images pp12, 16 (D.Young-Wollf), 71 (IM House), 72 (Hugh Sitton); Guardian Newspaper Ltd p26; Robert Harding Photolibrary p9; Mary Evans Picture Library pp36, 53; PA News Photolibrary/Dave Cheskin p76; Popperfoto p30; Save the Rhino p47; Science Photolibrary p6; Tony Stone/Ary Diesendruck p31.

Oxford University Press, Great Clarendon Street, Oxford OX2 6DP

Oxford   New York
Athens Auckland Bangkok Bogota Bombay Buenos Aires
Calcutta Cape Town Dar es Salaam Delhi Florence Hong Kong
Istanbul Karachi Kuala Lumpur Madras Madrid Melbourne
Mexico City Nairobi Paris Singapore Taipei Tokyo Toronto
Warsaw

and associated companies in
Berlin Ibadan

OXFORD and OXFORD ENGLISH are trade marks of Oxford University Press

With answers edition   ISBN 0 19 4328325
Classroom edition   ISBN 0 19 4328333

© Oxford University Press 1998

Printed at St Edmundsbury Press, UK

CONTENTS

A Read this article about genetic testing. Then decide whether the statements **1–7** are true or false, according to your understanding of the article.

1 The 'man of the future' is amazed by what the woman tells him.

2 The writer is talking about a situation which is extremely unlikely to exist in the next decade.

3 Our ability to understand human genes will produce only benefits for us.

4 The writer expected a more rapid conclusion to the results of the tests.

5 Tests showed that the writer could be prone to disease later in life.

6 Dr Trojanovsky was pessimistic about the writer's state of health.

7 The writer feels no more certain about her future health than she did before the tests.

how are your genes?

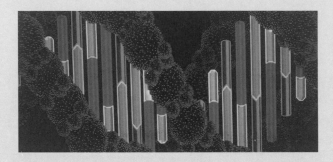

When Jocasta Shakespeare submitted herself to a laboratory test, she found there was a shock in store …

Just imagine a man and a woman sitting having a romantic meal in the year 2008. He says, "Has anyone
05 ever told you, you've got the most beautiful DNA?" She says, "There's something I've been meaning to tell you – I carry Apo E4 gene." He looks stunned,
10 as if she's suddenly developed halitosis. "You mean two copies?" She says, "Just one E4."

This is not science fiction. Within 10 years, genetic
15 screening will be widely available, as will profiles charting life span and death mode. You may want to know how long your partner is likely
20 to live and which disease he or she is programmed to die from. You might prefer to select one with a complementary genetic make-up, to provide your child
25 with the chance of a long life and resilience to dementia or heart disease.

As the discovery and testing of human genes escalates, we
30 will have to deal with new practical problems of insurance, employment contracts and confidentiality, as well as new moral questions about
35 euthanasia, abortion and eugenics. It is already technically possible to undergo 4,000 tests for genetic disorders to determine when you will die
40 and from which disease. But do you really want to know?

I decided to find out about my own life map from Dr Daniel Rader, who specializes in
45 genetic profiling for heart disease at Pennsylvania Medical Centre in Philadelphia. After what seems like an eternity, I am presented with the results of
50 the tests. The good news comes first. Dr Rader wears a nervous, big-toothed smile, trying hard to look relaxed. He congratulates me on "very
55 good" levels of cholesterol and an "excellent chemical battery"… the bad news is coming. "You have one copy of the Apo E4. This means a 30-per-
60 cent increased risk of heart disease. The E4 is also strongly predictive of Alzheimer's disease." Dr Rader refers me to Dr John Trojanovsky, Director of the
65 Alzheimer's Research Programme.

I find Dr Trojanovsky in a flippant mood. "Look on the bright side! Most people don't live to be 80 anyway," he says
70 cheerfully.

It is hard to come to terms with myself on a photocopied graph study. Will my life change as a result of my glance into this
75 crystal ball? Will I turn into a wet blanket, or become a real drag? I think not. After all, as Dr Trojanovsky philosophically points out, I could get run over
80 by a bus tomorrow. Perhaps the answer is to put a notice in the lonely hearts column: "Female (gorgeous), 35, excellent chemical battery, up to eight-
85 decade life span, with one copy of Apo E4, seeks E2 chap who supports euthanasia."

B Style. Find one example of each of the following devices, which the writer uses to create a more informal style in the article.

1 rhetorical questions, e.g. *What do they all have?*
2 imperatives, e.g. *Don't be*
3 slang, e.g. *mates*
4 direct address, e.g. *You (the reader) may*

What other devices does the writer use to involve the reader more actively in her experience?

C Vocabulary. The following words are all used in the article. Decide whether they are used to convey approval or disapproval by writing *app* or *dis* beside them. Then choose which option, A, B or C, is closest to the meaning of the words as they are used in the article. Use a dictionary if necessary.

EXAMPLE
   stunned (line 9)   *dis*
   A knocked (B) amazed C struck

1 *developed* (line 10)
   A grown B contracted C expanded

2 *complementary* (line 23)
   A corresponding B commendable C flattering

3 *resilience* (line 26)
   A elasticity B flexibility C immunity

4 *escalates* (line 29)
   A magnifies B increases C extends

5 *eternity* (line 48)
   A timelessness B ages C immortality

6 *nervous* (line 51)
   A agitated B excited C timid

7 *flippant* (line 67)
   A comical B disrespectful C irritable

8 *gorgeous* (line 83)
   A grand B beautiful C superb

D The writer refers to these *new moral questions* **(1–3).** Match them with the definitions in **a–c**.

1 euthanasia   **a** expelling a foetus from the womb

2 abortion   **b** improving the population by controlled breeding

3 eugenics   **c** making death gentler and easier for those in pain

Expressions with *come*

Complete these sentences using a suitable expression with *come*. The number of words needed is shown.

1 Some patients come _____ after an anaesthetic sooner than others.

2 Unfortunately Susan came _____ _____ 'flu just before she was due to go on holiday.

3 The children came _____ _____ some dreadful language after their visit to the cinema the other day.

4 Everyone began to wonder if the politician would ever come _____ _____ _____ in his speech.

5 Parents sometimes find it difficult to come _____ _____ _____ the fact that their children are not intelligent.

6 The judge came _____ _____ _____ the motorist, who was sentenced to five years in prison for causing the accident.

7 The new government policy on child care has come _____ _____ a lot of criticism.

8 Unless we can come _____ _____ something really original, the future of this company will be in jeopardy.

Structure

Rewriting

For each of the sentences below, write a new sentence as similar as possible in meaning using the word given in CAPITALS. This word must not be altered in any way.

1 The children prefer cycling to walking.

RATHER

_____

2 Don't eat so much fatty food and you won't have to try to lose weight.

SAVE

_____

3 When I saw the condition of the patient I realized how serious his illness was.

HOME

_____

4 We can avoid accidents by taking care when we cross the road.

PREVENTED

_____

5 Eating sensibly improves our health and increases our longevity.

ONLY

_____

6 You ought to go and see a doctor about those spots soon!

HIGH

_____

7 Similar interests brought Sue and Bob together initially.

COMMON

_____

8 The accident victim managed to pull through despite his serious condition.

ALTHOUGH

_____

9 Most people regard Dr Peters as being the best surgeon in his field.

WIDELY

_____

10 An argument between the management and the staff resulted in the postponement of the Annual General Meeting.

PUT

_____

Vocabulary

Parts of the body

Fill in the missing words for the appropriate parts of the body in this diagram.

Cloze and Summary

A Read this article about a place where animals are looked after. Fill each of the numbered blanks with <u>one</u> suitable word.

It's a DOG'S LIFE!

Donations from thousands of well-wishers have 1 _____ a part in funding an extension to the Battersea Dogs' Home. To a committed animal lover, the home might well be 2 _____ as one of the most dismal places in the city, and, to 3 _____ general public as a whole, the 4 _____ of so many badly treated animals ending up there is appalling. Yet the chances are that 5 _____ you think that, you have more than likely 6 _____ been there.

As 7 _____ as rescuing abandoned and injured animals, the home has, for a great many years, been recognized as a haven 8 _____ animals can feel renewed hope for the future. Although looking after the animals 9 _____ much patience and dedication, the staff are not in the business of making just 10 _____ visitors feel they would like to take home a pet on a whim. "We don't believe in merely recycling animals, so we aim 11 _____ the perfect match," says director Colonel Green, 12 _____ has a specially trained team to interview potential owners. People who have purchased pets there say that you instinctively know the one 13 _____ is right for you, just by watching them!

The brand new extension is 14 _____ to the eye, with the stress 15 _____ state-of-the-art quarters with heated beds and external exercise areas, neither of 16 _____ the animals have ever had before. The architects developed a much 17 _____ interest in the design after they had taken 18 _____ in the daily routine of looking after the animals, and helped out with various odd jobs, 19 _____ particular cleaning out the existing quarters. After all, there's only one way to improve a dog's life, and that's 20 _____ try it yourself!

B Summary. In about 40 words, summarize how people might feel initially about the Battersea Dogs' Home and why their feelings might change after a visit there.

Structure

Defining and non-defining clauses

Match sentences 1–5 with sentences a–e and join them using a relative pronoun.

1 The shaggiest dogs are a mixture of breeds.

2 In 1995, we were given no cause to celebrate.

3 Colonel Green has worked at the home for three and a half years.

4 Some animals look as if they have been through the mill.

5 The animals need new homes.

a He has also witnessed the ravages of war all over the world.

b Their owners have mistreated them.

c In that year, 2,044 dogs had to be put to sleep.

d They rub shoulders with the more exotic breeds.

e An affectionate stroke suggests new hope.

Write a short paragraph outlining the attitudes of people in
your country towards animals.

_____   _____
_____   _____
_____   _____
_____   _____
_____   _____
_____   _____
_____   _____
_____   _____

Vocabulary

animalcrackers

A Look at the words below. In which words are the letters *ram* pronounced or stressed differently?

cramp   framework   ramble

hologram   paramount

rampage   dramatic

pram   paramedic

gramophone

B Match the words with these meanings.

1 person who helps doctors
2 sudden and very noticeable
3 having supreme importance
4 structure giving shape and support
5 three-dimensional image

6 painful tightening of the muscles
7 record player
8 behave violently or destructively
9 baby carriage
10 walk in the countryside

2 FIRST IMPRESSIONS

Vocabulary

Time expressions

A Use these expressions connected with time to fill in the blanks in 1–4.

- *at the best of times*
- *buy time*
- *a bit pressed for time*
- *in time*

1 I'm sorry, but could we discuss your pay rise tomorrow? I'm _____ at the moment.

2 I'd like to make sure we get to the hotel _____ to unpack and have a shower before dinner.

3 I used to find Simon arrogant _____, but now that he has been promoted, he is quite unbearable.

4 I'm not ready to sign the contract yet – I think we should try and _____ by saying there are some legal problems that have to be sorted out.

B Now make up your own examples to show the meaning of these expressions.

- *time and time again*
- *for the time being*
- *in the nick of time*
- *on time*

1 _____
  _____
  _____
  _____

2 _____
  _____
  _____
  _____

3 _____
  _____
  _____
  _____

4 _____
  _____
  _____

Appearance and character

A Read passages 1–3. Which one was probably spoken by:
a an interviewer?
b someone talking about an acquaintance's new boyfriend?
c someone talking about a person they have forgotten?

1 ___ I didn't *think much of* him to be honest. He *struck me as being* rather shy and reserved, and he *looked* a bit timid. He's probably very sensitive and all the rest of it but he *gave me the impression of being* a bit dull for her.

2 ___ I must say, I felt he didn't *come across* very well; his reasons for wanting to join the firm were very vague, and he certainly didn't *seem* very bright. He *looked* much too casual, and actually he *reminded me a bit of* my Mr Jenkins, who lost us a lot of clients because he simply didn't *look like a* professional.

3 ___ I'm not even sure which one you are talking about… you're sure I met him, are you? Well, I suppose it just goes to show that he didn't exactly *make a big impression on me*.

B Look carefully at the expressions in *italics* in the three passages. Then rewrite the following sentences using the word in CAPITALS. This word must not be altered in any way.

1 The Minister doesn't make a good impression on TV.
ACROSS

_____

2 The candidate I interviewed appeared to lack ambition.
SEEM

_____

3 Pamela seemed to me to be rather insincere.
GAVE

_____

4 I felt that the last candidate seemed rather inexperienced.
STRUCK

_____

5 Some of Peter's expressions make me think of my brother.
REMIND

_____

6 You have obviously impressed Charlotte a great deal.
BIG

_____

SENDING MESSAGES IN THE HUMAN JUNGLE

When we walk through the city we are bombarded by stimuli of all kinds, such as traffic, crowds and noise, and most city dwellers experience a kind of information overload, which is dealt with by using an attentional filtering process. It is as if we have tunnel vision – we filter out the stimuli to those appearing at our central point of vision, or to those which are important to us. We don't stop, we keep our faces blank and eyes straight ahead, and in doing so, we are not just protecting ourselves but are avoiding overloading other people as well. We thus ignore certain things in the environment, and this applies particularly to things that regularly appear in the line of sight as we walk through the street. Commuters on their way to work may filter out or not even notice the sight of young people who have been sleeping rough in the same spot for some time.

When we are overloaded in the fast-moving, ever-changing environment of the city, we make use of stereotypes as convenient shorthand ways to make quick judgements about situations and people. They may not always be accurate, and they can often be dangerously wrong, but they are used regularly in a relatively benign way. Passing someone on the way to work, we may often summarise their social position and attitudes by briefly glancing at their dress, or the car they are driving or the newspaper they are reading.

The problem with the shorthand of stereotypes is that they restrict experience. By using limited clues to provide us with a rapid opinion of other people or places we may choose to limit our interactions. We may decide not to go to certain places because we believe they will not offer something we enjoy. However, the stereotypes we use offer a rapid way of summing up others without investing much energy or effort, and provide us with a way of dealing with the wide diversity of city life.

In the city, we not only use stereotypes to enable us to decode information but also make use of them in order to present an image of ourselves. When we are in public, we use dress and other non-verbal clues to create a stereotype that signals our social group, attitudes and personality to others. This enables us to make contact with other like-minded people and avoid others whom we regard as different.

In the context of the city, modes of dress are particularly important with regard to self-presentation. Different groups often use clearly identifiable styles of clothes so that they can be easily recognised. Using T-shirts and clearly labelled identifiers of places visited or affiliations are ways in which we can identify ourselves and have a clear opener for social interaction with others, and the structure of clothes is changing to cater for these needs. It is becoming increasingly common for brand names to be placed on the outside of garments, and this labelling makes it easy to transmit information about fashion and price instantly, and lets others tell at a distance whether an individual has similar tastes and is a suitable person to associate with.

Besides clothes, make-up and in particular hairstyle are all part of the process of giving off signals as to our group. The way the hair is worn in some traditional societies signals status and position, and in the city, hairstyles also signal group membership. Some other signals are much more subtle and may involve small differences in behaviour. In England, where social grouping or class continues to make social distinctions, people's accent and the manner of speaking are all clues to our social group. Class distinctions tend to be relatively fixed, although in the context of the city, where greater variety is permitted, they are more likely to be secondary determinants of friendship and association.

The Human Jungle by S Newman and S Lonsdale

A Read the passage opposite.

B **Multiple-choice questions.** Choose the best answer.

1 People walking in cities ignore much of the stimuli around them because
   A there is too much information to take in.
   B everyone else is expressionless.
   C the environment is already familiar to them.
   D they do not wish to talk to other people.

2 In the city, we assess people by using stereotypes because
   A we all have prejudices against certain groups.
   B they enable us to form reliable impressions of others.
   C we need to make judgements very quickly.
   D they need to be given the benefit of the doubt.

3 According to the text, the main disadvantage of using stereotypes is that they
   A may make us miss out on potentially pleasurable experiences.
   B have the potential of leading us into dangerous situations.
   C can rarely be relied upon.
   D make us mentally lazy.

4 In the city, clothes are particularly important because
   A they can help to create a particular stereotype.
   B they allow people to express their individuality.
   C they give a great deal of information about an individual.
   D people are becoming increasingly interested in fashion.

5 It would appear that in England, a person's class
   A is less relevant in an urban context.
   B is determined by their accent.
   C plays less of a role than it did in the past.
   D is something that can be changed easily.

C **Reference devices.** What do the words in *italics* refer to in the passage?

1 *which* is dealt with by using (line 6)
2 and in doing *so* (line 14)
3 *They* may not always be accurate (line 32)
4 *their* social position (line 38)
5 but also make use of *them* (line 60)
6 *This* enables us to make contact (line 65)
7 to cater for *these* needs. (line 81)
8 labelling makes *it* easy (line 85)

D **Summary.** In 60–80 words, summarize the advantages and disadvantages of relying on stereotypes to assess people in cities.

Structure

Rewriting

For each of the sentences below, write a new sentence as similar as possible in meaning using the word given in CAPITALS. This word must not be altered in any way.

1 Agnes was upset by some of her husband's religious views.

   FOUND

   _____

2 Do you know whose car that is?

   BELONG

   _____

3 I had intended to leave today, but I had to stay because of work.

   GOING

   _____

4 Dealers have been selling the new Mercedes since December.

   SALE

   _____

5 Oh, just go away! I'm getting very annoyed by you.

   BEING

   _____

6 I doubt whether you will have any trouble getting a visa.

   IMAGINE

   _____

7 The police have been watching the house for several weeks.

   SURVEILLANCE

   _____

8 In my opinion, the Prime Minister is not an exceptional leader.

   REGARD

   _____

9 The new terminal they are building will be finished next year.

   CONSTRUCTION

   _____

10 Apparently poverty and crime are linked.

   APPEARS

   _____

Vocabulary review

Choose the word which best completes each sentence.

1 At her trial in 1431 Joan of Arc was accused of being in
   ____ with the devil.
   A cooperation B association C league D conjunction

2 During the First World War, an ____ 5 million people
   lost their lives.
   A assumed B estimated C envisaged D approximated

3 The aim of the council's latest campaign is to ____ the
   use of the new recycling facilities.
   A project B prosecute C promote D provide

4 There was a great scandal when it turned out that the
   Bishop, who was meant to be ____, had a son.
   A celibate B singular C immaculate D separated

5 Mozart was a very ____ musician, and had written
   several concertos by the age of 10.
   A gifted B endowed C expert D qualified

6 According to psychiatrists, many violent criminals
   harbour feelings of ____ and insecurity.
   A insufficiency B shortage C inadequacy D scarcity

7 Many students find the concept of a fourth dimension
   difficult to ____.
   A hold B clutch C grab D grasp

8 If you want to be successful at writing complex
   computer programs, you need to adopt a more ____
   approach to your work.
   A systemic B systematic C synthetic D symptomatic

9 Charles Babbage's 'difference engine' is widely regarded
   as the ____ of modern computers.
   A precedent B precursor C ancestor D antecedent

10 The doctor told Harold that he had a mild chest
   infection and that there was no cause for ____.
   A anxiousness B worry C nervousness D concern

Cloze

Read the following book review and fill each of the numbered blanks with one suitable word.

One of the prominent themes of 20th century literature has been the future, and books **1** ____ as *Brave New World* by Aldous Huxley or *1984* by George Orwell have presented readers **2** ____ chilling visions of what may happen to society in the years **3** ____ .

The Handmaid's Tale, by science fiction writer Margaret Atwood, **4** ____ on this tradition and adds a feminist perspective. The novel is set in the futuristic Republic of Gilead, **5** ____ men have total power over women. The women of Gilead are no **6** ____ allowed to read; they may not leave home **7** ____ a permit, and the rulers **8** ____ sure that the women are kept in submission by the **9** ____ of violence. The system, at least in **10** ____ , is designed for the protection of women – to protect them from murder or rape. The **11** ____ of Gilead's women are infertile as a consequence of **12** ____ exposed to pesticides and nuclear waste. The women are classified **13** ____ to **14** ____ they can have children. The **15** ____ who can are taken to camps to be trained as 'Handmaids', **16** ____ role is to provide children for upper-class wives, while **17** ____ that are infertile become 'Marthas', or house servants.

The central **18** ____ is Offred, who becomes a Handmaid to a General and his wife, Serena Joy, after making an unsuccessful **19** ____ to escape from the Republic. The novel focuses **20** ____ their relationship, and in doing so the book addresses issues such as women's rights, the use of some reproductive technologies, and the role of women in a world that is still largely dominated by men.

animalcrackers

A Which initial letters need to be added to *eel* to make words which mean the following?

1 touch or sense
2 the back of the foot
3 a lively dance or a winding device
4 the base of a ship
5 remove the skin of fruit or vegetables

B Which letter could be substituted in the syllable *eel* without causing a change in pronunciation?

Writing

Character descriptions

Write three short character sketches based on the information below. For each one write:
  a a first paragraph, using the three adjectives given.
  b a second paragraph, including more details about the person using the prompts given.

EXAMPLE
  a use these adjectives: *dull, pedestrian, conventional*
  b talk about: the person's hobbies and interests

a Mr Jenkins, my old neighbour, was a very dull person who held only conventional ideas and led an extremely pedestrian life.

b It came as no great surprise when I discovered that his hobby was memorizing bus timetables; his knowledge of the subject was encyclopaedic. When asked, for example, how to get from one obscure part of the country to another on a wet Wednesday afternoon, he could detail precisely which buses one would have to take, where to change, and how long the journey would last, but he could never conceal the frisson of excitement that overcame him when he had met such a challenge.

1 **a** *frivolous, gregarious, vivacious*

_____

_____

b their gestures and reactions

_____

_____

_____

_____

2 **a** *boorish, moody, aggressive*

_____

_____

b their habits

_____

_____

_____

3 **a** *condescending, arrogant, snobbish*

_____

_____

b their attitudes and beliefs

_____

_____

_____

_____

SAFETY AND DANGER

A Read this article about a different kind of club.

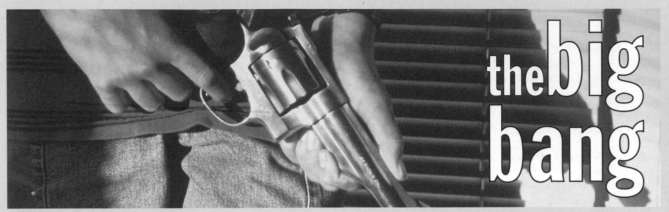

the big bang

City dwellers are discovering the benefits of a visit to a different kind of club. **Charlie Rushmore** *reports.*

There's something slightly disquieting about loading live bullets into a .357 at lunch time in the middle of a capital city. I was
05 brought up to detest violence, and to believe that shooting firearms is a morbid activity which is best avoided. Which is why I was determined not to enjoy myself at
10 the Mayfair Gun Club – and why I'm surprised to confess that I did. In fact, the Club is full of surprises – not least because it isn't anywhere near Mayfair.
15 Tucked beneath the railway arches at the back of a decaying housing estate in the dingiest of suburbs, this isn't the sort of place you'd glimpse by accident.
20 There are no signs that you can make out as you approach, merely a number on a door.

Gun clubs have traditionally suffered from a bad press and I
25 had telephoned the Club Secretary anticipating a less than favourable reply to my request to pay them a visit. His response, however, made it all seem as
30 controversial as indoor bowling.

'Sure,' he said. 'Come down whenever you like. We'll have a chat and give you a lesson.'
Once past the door, entry
35 phone and CCTV, I found myself in the Club lounge, where, apart from a small display of military memorabilia, it's silverware, not hardware that's on show. 'One of
40 the rules is that no military paraphernalia, uniforms or accessories are allowed in the Club,' says the owner. 'Once people have had a couple of
45 sessions, they realize it's not about aggression; it's about concentration, application. It's competitive, it's exciting, it's fun. The difference between this and
50 other clubs is that we tend not to attract gun enthusiasts. It's just another entertainment base. Most of our members have other interests.'
55 Firearm regulations in this country are among the tightest in the world, strictly controlling not only who uses guns, but where they're used. Setting up a gun
60 club in the first place is a serious business, and the nature of this game places substantial responsibilities on all concerned. The police must also be happy
65 with security. Safety is of paramount importance, and you're left under no illusion that if you break the rules, you're out.

The owner is an expert, I can
70 tell, and can obviously hit the bull's-eye with his eyes closed, so I reluctantly decide to have a go. Expecting to be knocked off my feet, I dig in and apply myself
75 rigorously to the task in hand, hoping to get it right. The noise is deafening, the recoil packs a punch, but by this time the bullet has found its way to the edge of
80 the black circle in the middle of the target. I stare at it in amazement. To my elation, my second knocks the centre out of the bull's-eye, and on that we call
85 it a day.
Politics on hold for a second, I have to admit that the experience was exciting and, after all, I'd done no harm. But when all's
90 said and done, I don't know whether firing guns can be said to be good, clean fun. Perhaps, with shooting, more than with most other pastimes, it depends
95 on your approach, and the all too familiar 'trigger-happy' psychology is a spectacular example of getting the approach wrong. The constitutional right
100 to bear arms creates a culture in which, even for recreational shooters, there lingers the notion that it's okay to shoot each other. The alternative approach
105 demands a different set of values.

Charlie Rushmore, *Livewire Magazine*

B Multiple-choice questions. Choose the best answer.

1 Charlie Rushmore confesses that
   A he was initially unable to find the gun club.
   B he has never written about firearms before.
   C he found his trip to the club entertaining.
   D he finds the sound of guns disturbing.

2 What had Charlie expected the Club Secretary to do?
   A invite him to inspect the premises
   B suggest that he joined the club
   C put him off paying the club a visit
   D tell the press about his visit

3 What comment does the owner make about the club?
   A The club is designed for those seeking recreation.
   B Gun enthusiasts find the club very entertaining.
   C Members of the Armed Forces are not allowed to join.
   D Club members have won many trophies.

4 According to Charlie, why is setting up a gun club difficult?
   A Firearms are difficult to obtain.
   B Applications take a long time to process.
   C You cannot afford to make any mistakes.
   D It is difficult to find suitable premises.

5 What happened during Charlie's shooting lesson?
   A He proved to be an accurate shot.
   B He was knocked off his feet by the recoil.
   C He hit the target with his eyes closed.
   D He needed guidance from his instructor.

6 What conclusion does Charlie come to about gun clubs?
   A They reflect our constitutional right to carry weapons.
   B They provide a harmless outlet for aggressive tendencies.
   C The idea will never be morally and ethically acceptable.
   D The attitude of the members is more important than the sport.

C Writing. Write a short paragraph expressing your opinion about gun clubs.

_____

_____

_____

_____

_____

_____

_____

_____

_____

D Synonyms. The words below all appear in the article. Can you explain what they mean? Use a dictionary if necessary.

1 disquieting _____

_____

2 morbid _____

_____

3 decaying _____

_____

4 less than favourable _____

_____

5 dingiest _____

_____

6 reluctantly _____

7 rigorously _____

_____

8 elation _____

_____

E Comprehension. The following expressions are used in the article. Can you explain what they mean in your own words?

1 *have suffered from a bad press* (line 24)

_____

2 *as controversial as indoor bowling* (line 30)

_____

3 *it's silverware, not hardware that's on show* (line 38)

_____

4 *the recoil packs a punch* (line 77)

_____

5 *we call it a day* (line 84)

_____

6 *all too familiar 'trigger-happy' psychology* (line 95)

_____

F Summary. In 50–60 words, summarize how the writer felt about firearms before and after his visit to the gun club.

Related word groups

The words *glimpse, make out* and *stare* are used in the article on page 16. Match the letters on the left (**a–h**) with those on the right (**i–p**) to form words to do with using your eyes. Then choose suitable explanations for these words from **1–8** below.

a	gl	**i**	er
b	wi	**j**	ze
c	p	**k**	mpse
d	bl	**l**	re
e	ga	**m**	ance
f	gli	**n**	eep
g	pe	**o**	nk
h	sta	**p**	ink

1 look steadily at, rudely perhaps
2 see briefly
3 close one eyelid only
4 have a quick look
5 take a quick look (e.g. through a keyhole)
6 look closely to see more clearly
7 close the eyelids rapidly
8 look at intently or longingly

Rewriting: Expressions with *do*

For each of the sentences below, write a new sentence as similar as possible in meaning using the word given in CAPITALS. This word must not be altered in any way.

1 Why do I always get the boring jobs? I'm fed up with it.
DONKEY

_____

2 No one ever benefited from being poor!
GOOD

_____

3 My brother kindly lent me his car for the weekend.
FAVOUR

_____

4 She looks great with that new hairstyle.
WONDERS

_____

5 Decorating has really improved this room.
UP

_____

6 Doctors say that smoking is bad for your health.
HARM

_____

7 Richard is a real expert at laying carpets now.
CLOSED

_____

8 If it hadn't been for your help, I couldn't have written the book.
WITHOUT

_____

9 The thief was sent to prison for the crimes he had committed.
TIME

_____

10 Teachers think that hard work is good for you.
HARM

_____

Read this article about falling asleep while driving. Fill each of the numbered blanks with <u>one</u> suitable word.

THE TWILIGHT ZONE

It's that dangerous moment that drivers fear most: nodding [1]_____ at the wheel. Falling asleep at the wheel could account for [2]_____ than 20 per cent of accidents on dull, monotonous roads such as motorways, [3]_____ to a recent medical report. Typically, these involve running off the road or into the back of another vehicle, and are more [4]_____ to cause serious injury owing to the sleepy driver's failure to brake. Of course it is a [5]_____ that the body's biological clock has a major influence, as these accidents peak at [6]_____ when sleepiness is naturally higher. Although I have never [7]_____ this happen to me, men under 30 are the most vulnerable, as they are the drivers most typically out on the roads in the early hours. Apparently, they take more risks in driving [8]_____ sleepy (it must be added, [9]_____, that alcohol is not a factor here).

In contrast, older people suffer [10]_____ an early afternoon 'dip', when they are more [11]_____ risk.

Time-of-day was found to be as important as the length of the drive, yet practical advice to drivers often concentrates more [12]_____ the length of the drive than its timing.

Devices are now [13]_____ marketed as in-car monitors of driver sleepiness, ostensibly to warn drivers, but doubts are being [14]_____ about these devices. What is the [15]_____ of alerting drivers already aware that they are sleepy but who still persist [16]_____ driving? What is [17]_____, these devices are of unproven reliability and may simply encourage drivers to take further risks. Not [18]_____ does driving motivate tired drivers into putting more effort into remaining awake, but, in this kind of [19]_____, sleep onset can be delayed and distorted. The best advice is either to find some [20]_____ not to drive at night, or to get the car off the road as soon as possible, if you're not feeling too bright and breezy!

Expressions to do with the weather

Each of the following expressions includes one wrong word.
Correct the expressions and then match them with their
meanings **a–h.**

1 get breeze of
2 light and breezy
3 It's a sick wind that blows nobody any good.
4 the peace before the storm
5 a storm in a glass
6 do heavy weather of
7 below a cloud
8 under the climate

a not feeling well
b Although it seems like a disaster, somebody will benefit
   from it.
c find out about something
d Don't be deceived by the fact that it's quiet!
e in disgrace
f a lot of fuss about nothing
g find very difficult
h extremely cheerful

Blank-filling: Uses of *have* and *got*

Fill each of the blanks with a suitable phrase using *have* or *got*.
Sometimes, both are possible.

1 I _____ at the local garage yesterday.

2 I've never _____ stop me for speeding
   before!

3 I won't _____ driving my new car.

4 We _____ all the children asking for chips
   if we walk past the burger bar now!

5 I _____ broken into last night.

6 I _____ to cut the grass in the garden for
   me yesterday.

7 I _____ cut at that expensive hairdresser's
   in town last Saturday.

8 I'm going _____ the plumber to fix that
   leaking tap tomorrow.

Vocabulary

animalcrackers

ebullient

bull's-eye

bulletin

bullet   bullion

bully

bullfinch

bulldoze

Write synonyms or paraphrases to explain the meanings of these words.
Use your dictionary if necessary.

STRANGER THAN FICTION

Vocabulary

Complete this puzzle to find the missing word.

1 A person who has _____ powers can perform spiritualistic feats.

2 A _____ can say what will happen to you in the future.

3 Your _____ is based on the positions of the stars and planets at the time of your birth.

4 A strong feeling forewarning you about a future event is called a _____ .

5 A _____ is someone who can see things in their mind that are happening at a different time or place.

6 A _____ is someone who can tell things about you by studying the lines in your hand.

7 The _____ is a word that describes everything that is supernatural, mystical and magical.

8 A person with _____ powers can communicate with others at a distance through the mind.

9 An _____ illusion is an image that is not what it seems.

10 A _____ is a person who can communicate with the spirit world.

11 A house that is haunted has a _____ in it.

12 A _____ is a meeting of a group of people who are attempting to contact the spirit world.

Cloze

Fill each of the numbered blanks with <u>one</u> suitable word.

HONGCHENG MAGIC LIQUID

We live in a supposedly scientific age, but there is a growing tide of irrationalism and hostility 1 _____ science. In spite of – or perhaps 2 _____ of the achievements of science in unravelling the mysteries of life, the attitudes of the general public bear many striking 3 _____ to beliefs that were held in the Middle Ages. There is widespread conviction that proof of the paranormal does 4 _____, but that it is being withheld.

An example of this is the case of 'Hongcheng Magic Liquid', a latter-day version of the medieval alchemist's stone. In the 1980s, a simple man from China named Wang Hongcheng 5 _____ to have discovered a cheap and plentiful compound that 6 _____ turn ordinary water 7 _____ petrol. When the authorities 8 _____ wind of this intriguing liquid, they agreed to provide the funds for further research. However, when the experiments took 9 _____, it quickly became apparent that the whole operation had been 10 _____ but an elaborate 11 _____, and Wang Hongcheng was thrown into prison. The public, however, 12 _____ from being disillusioned with Wang Hongcheng, began to regard him 13 _____ a legendary figure. They were firmly convinced that he could do what he claimed and concluded that the government 14 _____ have imprisoned him simply because of his 15 _____ to tell them the secret of how it was made.

Accusations 16 _____ government secrecy and cover-ups are widespread in the West as well. The phenomenally successful TV programme *The X Files* is 17 _____ upon the premise that work on the paranormal is in fact being 18 _____ out, although this is being done 19 _____ secret. The idea is powerful because it explains the almost total 20 _____ of scientific proof of paranormal phenomena; it suggests that the proof has been there all the time, but they have been keeping it from us.

Everyone knows that towards the end of his presidency Ronald Reagan could hardly make a move without consulting an astrologer. However, the mind boggles at the possibility that the British government might use a hotline to psychic powers. Nevertheless, it has been revealed that British Intelligence is in contact with a self-styled 'psychic dreamer' who supplies them with advance information on important crimes that are about to happen.

The man with the premonitory antennae is Chris Robinson, a 44-year-old former television engineer. He seems an unlikely candidate for a real-life version of *The X-Files* but he has had some startling successes with his predictions.

Dreams provide the key. According to Robinson, it all began in the late 80s, when his slumbers were interrupted by 'conversations' with his dead grandmother. Later his dreams were invaded by a range of symbols which enabled him to predict specific crimes. Terrorists were represented by dogs, cups signified bodies, meat pies chillingly foreshadowed multiple deaths and images of cats or dogs indicated that fanatical animal liberationists were at work.

Robinson decided to share the messages from his subconscious with the authorities and warned them of a crime that was about to take place. When his predictions came true a few days later, he was rewarded by being detained and interrogated; he claims that his home was bugged, his telephone was tapped, and he was subjected to 24-hour surveillance.

Undaunted by this scepticism, he carried on with his work and warned the authorities of an imminent attack on the Prime Minister with uncanny accuracy. Subsequently he was given a contact in the police and Intelligence Service, and has been handsomely rewarded for his services.

Doubts about Robinson's methods have been raised by the revelations that in the 80s he was an enthusiastic amateur radio fan, and he frequently used equipment that could be used to intercept calls from mobile phones and the emergency services. Indeed, on one occasion, he phoned with a prediction of a crime that had in fact already happened, and details had been broadcast on the radio and TV.

However, Dr Keith Hearne, an independent psychologist, has taken a special interest in Robinson's predictions. He has observed the psychic at work as he scribbles down the images he has dreamt for later decoding. Hearne believes that Robinson has genuine powers, but admits that he has an understandable tendency to emphasise his successes while evading questions on the ones that got away. Of one thing Hearne is certain: Robinson has an impressively accurate record when it comes to terrorist attacks.

While the intelligence services and police forces deny that they have any official links with Robinson, they admit that they have been in touch. It will always be difficult for them to determine whether he has any genuinely paranormal powers as he operates in a grey area where sheer guesswork, intuition and possibly telepathy could all play a part, and his dreams are always symbolic and open to interpretation.

But when he phones again, we can be certain someone will listen.

Robin Cross, *Livewire Magazine*

A Read the text and say which of these four titles would be the most suitable.
1 Optical Illusions
2 The Dream Detective
3 Horror Scopes
4 Spy in the Sky

B Multiple-choice questions. Choose the best answer.

1 The writer appears to be extremely surprised that
   A Ronald Reagan appeared to believe in horoscopes.
   B the British authorities have links with a psychic.
   C psychics can provide warnings of important crimes.
   D important information has been kept secret from the public.

2 Robinson seems to obtain his detailed predictions by
A 'talking' to his dead grandmother while he dreams.
B communicating with animals in his dreams.
C interpreting images in his dreams.
D analysing the crimes he sees in his dreams.

3 The authorities' initial reaction to Robinson's claims indicate that they thought he
A was personally involved with the crimes.
B had a contact in the intelligence service.
C had paranormal powers.
D was obtaining information by tapping phones.

4 The authorities' attitude towards Robinson changed
A when they began to pay him for his services.
B when they had examined the methods he was using.
C after another of his predictions came true.
D on the orders of the Prime Minister.

5 Investigations of Robinson's supposed psychic abilities have shown that
A he always makes use of conventional methods to obtain information.
B his only successful predictions are based on facts that are already known.
C he dislikes discussing predictions that turn out to be correct.
D he appears to be really able to foresee some kinds of crime.

6 The writer appears to think that
A Robinson is a genuine psychic.
B the authorities should be more open about their relationship with Robinson.
C the authorities should take more notice of Robinson.
D it would be unwise to dismiss Robinson completely.

C Language study. The phrase *without consulting an astrologer* appears in the text. Complete the following sentences using one of the words or phrases below.

- *without*   - *on*   - *between*
- *in spite of* - *by*   - *apart from*

1 _____ waking, I always write down my dreams so that I don't forget them.

2 I never make an important decision _____ looking at my horoscope first.

3 _____ being very sceptical, the authorities agreed to look at the psychic's claims.

4 The police believe that Simon committed the crime _____ leaving the office and arriving home.

5 The gypsy claimed she could predict the future _____ reading the lines in my palm.

6 _____ giving the police general details of what was about to happen, he could not provide any useful information.

D Summary. In 60–80 words, summarize the differing reactions to Robinson's powers.

Structure

Rewriting

For each of the sentences below, write a new sentence as similar as possible in meaning using the word given in CAPITALS. This word must not be altered in any way.

1 It's possible that John wasn't feeling well.

MIGHT

_____

2 Mary had the talent to become a concert pianist, but she didn't really want to.

COULD

_____

3 It's very annoying that you didn't tell me you had changed your plans.

TOLD

_____

4 It was wrong of me to speak to her like that.

SPOKEN

_____

5 You ran the risk of killing yourself by touching that wire.

COULD

_____

6 It turned out that I had been worrying about my cat unnecessarily.

WORRIED

_____

7 If he hadn't followed you home, he wouldn't know where you live.

MUST

_____

8 I should have picked Jane up from the station, but I completely forgot about it.

SUPPOSED

_____

MAD or BAD ?

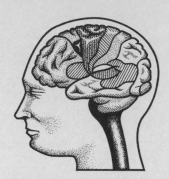

A It was not so very long ago in our history that we locked away the mentally ill and kept them in chains. We know better now – that mental
05 illness is not a God-given sign of evil and turpitude. But if crime is – to any extent – the result of neurophysical or chemical factors beyond our control, then it is illogical for us to deal with
10 whole categories of criminals in the way that we do.

B There is certainly evidence that chemical factors play a major role in criminal behaviour. At the forefront of
15 current research is the neurotransmitter serotonin, which in the normal mind has the effect of regulating impulsive behaviour. It acts like a brake or controlling
20 mechanism, and individuals whose serotonin levels are abnormally low tend to demonstrate patterns of antisocial behaviour. In young children, this manifests itself as
25 aggressiveness, restlessness, throwing tantrums or cruelty towards animals. Adolescents with low serotonin levels are prone to attention disorders in school and to sensation-seeking that
30 often involves vandalism, car theft and petty crime. Repeated studies have shown a strong link between low serotonin levels and delinquency.

C Apart from the effect of chemicals,
35 the study of the effects of brain damage – whether it has been caused by genetic inheritance, birth complications, actual accidents or disease – can give us an insight into
40 the abnormal brain and its links with criminal behaviour. The brain is a massively complex organ, but recent investigations have dramatically increased our awareness of the
45 function of different parts of the brain. We know that damage to the left side of the brain can lead to schizophrenia and sexual deviation; damage to the right side, where the
50 emotions are stored, can cause severe manic depression. If the front of the brain is affected this can lead to a lack of self control, aggressive and psychopathic behaviour, while
55 damage to the temporal lobes may cause epilepsy, delusions, or hearing voices, a common symptom of schizophrenia.

D In Canada, a study was carried out by
60 the clinical neuropsychologist Professor Yeudall of over 2,000 criminals who had not responded to attempts to rehabilitate them, and who in consequence returned time
65 after time to prison. What became startlingly clear was the high incidence of deficit and dysfunction in the brains of these patients. The consistency was staggering – brain
70 damage was identified in 90% of the 2,000.

E The effects of serotonin levels and of brain damage are only two elements of the immensely complex area of
75 biological factors in crime, but the knowledge that we have already gained raises a colossal new agenda. What are we to do with our traditional, reassuring moral
80 judgements and our comfortable assumptions of good and evil? If criminals are sick, should we punish them any more than we should discriminate against the physically
85 disabled? Would it be right to treat crime with the effective drugs we already have, which would save tens of thousands of pounds per year, or is there a deep sense that somehow
90 treatment 'excuses' criminality and robs us of some need to punish?

F The evidence that biology is a central factor to crime, interacting with cultural, social and economic factors,
95 is so strong that to ignore it is perverse. As perverse, indeed, as to cling to the mysteries of astrology long after the astronomer's telescope has opened our eyes.

A Mind to Crime by D Jessel and A Moir

A Read this text.

B Match these headings with the paragraphs in the text.

1 The influence of chemicals on behaviour

2 The moral issues raised by research

3 Changing attitudes towards mental illness

4 The effects of damage to different areas of the brain

5 The need for a change in attitudes towards crime

6 Strong evidence of a link between brain damage and criminal behaviour

1	2	3	4	5	6

C Answer these comprehension questions.

1 What does the author mean by saying that *mental illness is not a God-given sign of evil and turpitude*? (line 4)

2 Explain the meaning of the phrase *At the forefront of current research*. (line 14)

3 What effect do normal levels of serotonin have?

4 What does *this* refer to in line 24?

5 Explain in your own words *recent investigations have dramatically increased our awareness of the function of different parts of the brain*. (line 42)

6 Why are the results of Professor Yeudall's study described as *staggering*? (line 69)

7 Explain in your own words *the knowledge that we have already gained raises a colossal new agenda*. (line 76)

Vocabulary review

Choose the word which best completes each sentence.

1 By making it easier to trace who is phoning, companies have reduced the number of ___ calls.
A evil B malignant C malicious D wicked

2 The acrobats at the circus performed some very impressive ___ .
A deeds B exploits C actions D feats

3 People suffering from claustrophobia are afraid of being in ___ spaces.
A compressed B confined C diminished D reduced

4 I'm not sure my brother will ever get married because he hates the feeling of being ___ .
A tied up B tied in C tied in with D tied down

5 The police are treating the accident as suspicious because they have found out that the brakes had been ___ with.
A altered B tampered C meddled D modified

6 The footballer ___ in agony on the pitch, and it was clear that his knee had been broken.
A wriggled B writhed C squirmed D twisted

7 The doctor diagnosed that the patient was suffering from a ___ case of food poisoning.
A grave B heavy C harsh D severe

8 By using all the latest technology, the yachtsman managed to cross the Atlantic in ___ time.
A quickest B lightning C top D record

Structure

Blank-filling: Chance and probabilities

Fill each of the blanks in the following sentences with a suitable word or phrase.

1 It seems to me that the result of the match _____ conclusion.

2 I _____ whether my brother will pass his driving test as he's terribly nervous.

3 _____ probability there will be an election soon because the government is in deep trouble.

4 I _____ thought that John would come on holiday with us because he hates flying.

5 You're bright and you've worked very hard so you're _____ your exam.

6 Jean is _____ to know where her brother is living because they haven't been on speaking terms for years.

Vocabulary

animalcrackers

A In which words are the letters *bat* pronounced or stressed differently?

com**bat**   **bat**tery   re**bat**e   **bat**hrobe

batch   pro**bat**ion   sab**bat**ical   pro**bat**e

B Match the words with these meanings.

a a set of jobs done at the same time by a computer
b a loose garment worn before or after washing
c a period of time given at intervals for study or travel, e.g. to university teachers
d fighting between two people, armies, etc.
e the official process of proving that a will is correct
f an amount by which a debt or tax can be reduced
g a legal system whereby a guilty person has to report to an official for a fixed time
h a device that contains and supplies electricity

C Words which go together. Which words in **A** above could combine with each of the words below?

1 a flat _____
2 a tax _____
3 to grant _____
4 _____ processing
5 a year's _____
6 a silk _____
7 to be put on _____
8 unarmed _____

D Choose four of the word combinations above and use them in sentences of your own.

Have fridge, will travel

From the time the first settlers gaped from the top of the Appalachian Mountains at the limitless vista opening 05 westwards, America has been a society obsessed with travel. What is the point of going to one of the world's great countries, with roads stretching clear to a distant 10 horizon, if not to drive?

I have driven many times in the US, but have never before taken on one of the large motor caravans – known as RVs (recreation vehicles) 15 – which roll like modern covered wagons along the interstates all summer long. We rented an intermediate RV – big enough for six. It was by no means the largest 20 or most sophisticated available: some of the outrageous chrome giants that passed us on the highway were almost as large as coaches and seemed to have rather 25 more mod cons than the Starship Enterprise.

It may be three or four generations since the first intrepid settlers trudged west across the 30 prairies, struggled over the high sierras and staggered through the desert to the Californian Nirvana,

but in a motorhome you can get an illusion that the pioneering 35 spirit still applies. That is, if you discount the comforts of air-conditioning, the double beds, the shower and the toilet that come as standard fittings. The campsites 40 have swimming pools and electricity, water and sewage hook-ups. Mark you, you can still get a hint of the pioneering days. As you do not generally collect your RV 45 before mid-afternoon, by the time you take charge, you can't wait to get under way. Having expected to collect ours in the morning, we had stupidly booked a campsite 50 220 miles away across the desert – much too ambitious for exhausted parents and tired children to attempt in the late afternoon. We picked up our RV in downtown Los 55 Angeles, lumbered slowly down the freeways amid the rush-hour traffic and set out across the desert to our distant campsite. In retrospect, I wish we'd checked that we could 60 work the air-conditioning system first. August, in the middle of the desert, with the temperature still well over 100°F at 11 p.m., is not the best time to discover that you

65 can't make it work. We ploughed, rather dejectedly, across the desert for a couple of hours in the appalling heat and descended through the haze to the gleaming 70 minarets and neon signs of Las Vegas, noting grimly that the temperature was touching 112°F. Why have mechanics the world over the same perverse contempt 75 for the ignorant amateur? Is it innate or are they coached? Ours, with a deep sigh, pointed condescendingly to a deceptively simple switch we'd missed, told us 80 we really ought to have moved the dial in a different direction, and three minutes later sent us on our way with a wave. 'Look on the bright side! It could have been 85 worse,' we shouted to each other over the new roar of the air-conditioning. 'We might have had to spend the night in Las Vegas.'

The roads of the formerly wild 90 West are amazingly open, stretching out ahead in a straight line for 30 miles. Driving in the US is, anyway, straightforward. There are surprisingly few hitches for the 95 unwary: no roundabouts and a more leisurely pace created by the 55 mph limit. In such an enormous wilderness, you are unlikely to meet congestion once 100 you leave the cities, though you may be terrified by the competitive driving of the juggernauts. You pass them labouring up the hill, then they pass you on the 105 downslope as if outraged by your cheek at overtaking them. One nearly ran us off the road when its lane on the freeway merged into ours.

110 I would not kid you that the motorhomes are particularly easy to drive. But, we arrived back safe and sound and convinced that an RV is a good way to see the scenic 115 wonders of the US for around the same price as hiring a car and trying to find a decent motel every night!

Stephen Bates, *The Guardian Weekend*

A Quickly read the article by Stephen Bates about a tour of the not-so-wild West. Then choose the best answer to this question.

Stephen's conclusion about motorhomes is that they are:
   a too cumbersome to drive well.
   b too luxurious for the holiday-maker.
   c an acceptable form of transport.
   d the cheapest way to see the US.

B Multiple-choice questions. Read the article again and choose the best answers to questions **1–6**.

1 According to Stephen, how did the first settlers feel as they viewed the scene from the Appalachians?
   A confused   B resigned   C reassured   D amazed

2 What appears to be Stephen's attitude to the more sophisticated RVs?
   A envy   B respect   C disapproval   D indifference

3 What seems to be Stephen's attitude to the original pioneering spirit?
   A admiration   B contempt   C amusement   D irritation

4 Stephen's attitude towards mechanics is one of
   A condescension.   B resentment.   C gratitude.
   D resignation.

5 Stephen looks back on the episode regarding the air-conditioning with
   A amusement.   B anger.   C pride.   D regret.

6 Which adjective best sums up the mood of the article?
   A hilarious   B positive   C argumentative   D disparaging

C Comprehension. Explain these phrases from the article in your own words.

   1 *a society obsessed with travel* (line 6)

   _____

   _____

   2 *the outrageous chrome giants* (line 21)

   _____

   _____

   3 *we ploughed, rather dejectedly* (line 65)

   _____

   _____

   4 *in the appalling heat* (line 67)

   _____

   _____

   5 *noting grimly* (line 71)

   _____

   _____

   6 *the same perverse contempt* (line 74)

   _____

   _____

   7 *pointed condescendingly* (line 77)

   _____

   _____

   8 *to a deceptively simple switch* (line 78)

   _____

   _____

   9 *you are unlikely to meet congestion* (line 98)

   _____

   _____

   10 *as if outraged by your cheek at overtaking them* (line 105)

   _____

   _____

D Summary. Stephen Bates mentions four difficulties or problems he encountered. In about 80 words, summarize these problems. Use appropriate linking words and phrases in your answer.

E Related word groups. Stephen Bates uses the following words in connection with driving. Can you supply the missing letters?

1 o __ __ rt __ __ e

2 t __ __ d __ e

3 s __ __ u __ __ __ c

4 s __ __ gg __ r

5 l __ m __ __ r

6 l __ b __ __ r

7 p __ ou __ h

8 d __ __ c __ __ d

Which words are used in a negative sense?

Now match the words with these explanations.

a work hard
b try hard
c make slow progress
d go down
e walk unsteadily as if about to fall
f pass
g walk with difficulty, e.g. through snow
h move in a slow, clumsy, noisy way

Only one of these words is normally used in connection with driving. Which one?

Prefixes and suffixes

A Which prefixes on the left can be used with the words on the right?

	comfortable
mis-	comfort
	honest
dis-	noble
	adventurous
ig-	ability
	ambitious
un-	likely
	manage
in-	interesting

B Which words on the left can be used with which suffix(es) on the right?

worth	
resent	
hope	-ful
youth	-less
stress	
point	

C Use three words from A and three from B in sentences of your own.

Vocabulary

animalcrackers

gigantic   avant-garde   triumphant   rampant
significant   frantic   enchanting   romantic

Complete sentences 1–8 using the words above.

1 The climbers returned _____ after their successful ascent of the mountain.

2 As there were seven in our party, we rented the most _____ mobile home we could find.

3 We were in such a(n) _____ rush when we left that we forgot the airline tickets!

4 There have been some _____ improvements in the comfort of air travel over the last decade.

5 That new Shakespeare production is so _____ than nobody has a clue which play it's supposed to be!

6 The setting of Taormina, a small town in Sicily, is one of the most _____ in the world and has attracted many honeymooners this year.

7 Unfortunately, malaria is _____ at this time of year in that part of the world.

8 The young dancers looked so _____ in their costumes that we took masses of photographs of them.

Structure

Transformations

Finish each sentence in such a way that it means exactly the same as the one before it.

1 We were stupid to leave for the airport so late.

I wish _____

_____

2 Why didn't we rent a smaller motorhome?

If only _____

_____

3 John was going to check the departure times but he forgot.

John regrets _____

_____

4 Please stop complaining about the heat!

I wish _____

_____

5 We are sorry but your tickets have been mislaid.

We regret to _____

_____

6 It always takes so long to fill in travel insurance documents.

I wish _____

7 Don't tell me what to do!

I wish _____

_____

8 Travelling can be so exhausting!

I wish _____

_____

Blank-filling

Fill each of the blanks in the following sentences with a suitable word or phrase.

1 It's difficult _____ side when the temperature's 112°F!

2 Drivers of larger RVs tend _____ noses at other drivers.

3 The driver discovered to his horror that _____ petrol.

4 The security cameras had _____ red-handed.

5 The tourists _____ rats after their walk in the rain.

6 The excited children _____ to travelling across the US.

7 The passengers finally _____ and sound.

8 The explorers were none _____ for their harrowing experience in the desert.

Cloze Revision

The following words appeared in previous Cloze exercises. Do you remember their meaning?

Unit 1

dismal

_____

a haven

_____

on a whim

_____

Unit 2

chilling

_____

Unit 3

nodding off

_____

ostensibly

_____

onset

_____

Unit 4

unravelling

_____

get wind of

_____

Cloze development

Twenty words are missing in the following article. Mark a / to show where the words should be and write the words at the bottom of the article.

A GREAT POLAR
EXPLORER

The most famous British polar explorer/Captain Scott (1868–1912), a naval officer who led two expeditions to the Antarctic. The first expedition left England in August 1901 aboard the *Discovery*, a specially built wooden. Scott's companions were Shackleton, who himself became famous as Antarctic explorer, and the doctor, naturalist and artist Edward Wilson. They discovered the great ice-cap surrounding South Pole and reached a point further south anyone before them. Then, with their food running and the dogs that pulled their sledge exhausted, they turned and struggled back. Scott preparations for another Antarctic journey. The second expedition sailed in the whaling ship *Terra Nova*, and set a large base ashore on Ross Island in 1911. Before the winter, the expedition laid out 'depots', or piles food and fuel the way towards the Pole. The polar journey began on November 1. The expedition had motor sledges and ponies as well dogs for hauling the ordinary sledges, but the motors broke down after few days. The decision to ponies rather than dogs to pull the sledges on the final stages of the journey was prove fatal. The expedition was unlucky the weather and was delayed very low temperatures and blizzards. The supporting party turned back leaving Scott to out pulling a sledge with four companions. Towards the end of their ordeal, their food and fuel exhausted, Scott wrote: 'for own sake, I, myself, not regret this journey'. In the following spring a search party from the base managed to their bodies. They also recovered Scott's letters and diaries. The heroic end aroused the admiration of world.

was

Write a short paragraph describing the best/worst/most interesting journey you have ever made. Pay particular attention to your choice of verbs and adjectives, selecting those which will express your feelings about the journey most vividly.

_____

_____

_____

_____

_____

_____

_____

_____

_____

ART FOR ART'S SAKE

Cloze

A Read the text about the Stone of Destiny and answer these questions.

1 In what way is the Stone of Destiny valuable?

2 In what sense is the Stone of Destiny not valuable?

3 What use did the English make of the Stone?

4 Why is it sometimes complicated to decide whether a work of art should be returned?

5 What do we learn about the financial resources of the Getty Museum?

6 Which particular objects does the writer think should be returned?

B Now fill each of the numbered blanks with one suitable word.

When the Stone of Destiny came back to Scotland, it was the culmination of a 700-year campaign to __1_____ it returned. The Stone, which is little __2_____ than a lump of rock of no great commercial __3_____ or artistic merit, is of great symbolic __4_____ to the Scottish people, who, according to legend, could never be free while it was still __5_____ held on foreign soil. It had originally been stolen by the English King Edward I in 1296. Prior __6_____ its repatriation, it was kept in Westminster Abbey in London, where it was used during coronations of English monarchs and on other ceremonial __7_____ but its absence from its __8_____ home was a continual __9_____ of grievance to the Scots.

The return of the Stone has once again raised the question of __10_____ should be done about other national treasures held in museums and private collections abroad. Sometimes the __11_____ under which an item was __12_____ make the decision simple; if it was stolen, it should go back. But more often than not the situation is far __13_____ straightforward. Artistic treasures may have been bought from colonial governments who had no moral __14_____ to sell them, or donated by principalities and countries that no __15_____ exist.

There is also a moral problem here. The Getty museum, with its vast resources, could in all __16_____ buy the entire artistic heritage of Bangladesh quite legitimately, and __17_____ this would __18_____ most reasonable people as being questionable. The __19_____ of every work of art being returned to its country of origin are remote, but nations should have a right to house treasures of supreme cultural significance. As the return of the Stone of Destiny shows, this can be achieved, but not __20_____ a struggle.

THE GRAND TOUR

Literally speaking, 'grand tour' means 'big journey', a French phrase because in the latter half of the eighteenth century, at the time of its flourishing, all educated people spoke French (and, if they were male, had a knowledge of Latin and often Greek). For the well-born young men setting off on their Grand Tour, it was indeed a big journey, one that would take them all round Europe and give them the opportunity to learn the nature and significance of their own cultural roots. It was a cultural search in the broadest sense. These youths were thought to be, in an age innocent of democracy, the future leaders of the country, and it was essential that they should understand their heritage as fully as possible.

They did not venture out alone, however. The Grand Tourists travelled with an entourage, prominent among whom was the tutor, the scholarly cleric whose task it was to foster the educational purposes of the journey. The Grand Tour could – and did – last for several years, involving prolonged residence in the sites of special importance. Athens was high on this list, as indeed were Rome and the major cities of Italy, from which so much of our civilisation has come. It was intended to be a serious learning process, a secular version of the pilgrimages of the religious past, and if it seemed often to fail in this, the same comment could be levelled at those very pilgrimages. Preachers in the Middle Ages were always thundering denunciations of pilgrims who appeared primarily bent on the excitements of travel, seekers of pleasure rather than grace. For the most enlightened, the two ends probably did not seem uncomplementary.

Through the kindness of the BBC, I probably travelled in greater comfort than the wealthy milord, who bumped along the rough roads of pre-industrial Europe in a lumbering carriage, staying at flea-infested inns and encountering the hazards of a foreign menu. And of course, I could never have gone on my own, asking the Carmelite sisters at Quidenham to pay for me, however intense my desire.

Yet, let me confess, the desire was not all that intense. The Grand Tour is essentially for the young, whose stamina is up to its surprises. Not only am I an ancient of 1930s vintage, but I have chosen a lifestyle which offers the bliss of living alone in prayer. That is a happiness so real, so humbling, that no other experience, however splendid, can compare. When kind people asked me if I was enjoying myself on my Grand Tour, I all too often found it hard to say 'yes'. I would then feel ashamed of seeming so ungrateful, and after much tactless honesty, I found the truthful answer. I would say 'Yes, relatively.' Of itself, absolutely, I would never want to leave my solitude. But relatively, since it had become clear to me that there was a certain value for people in what I said about art, then I accepted with gratitude this great chance to see some of the most wonderful things that human beings have ever created. Now that the travelling is over, and I am back in silence again, the memories are happy ones.

In making my programmes, I hoped to be a tool for people to see through, a sort of human magnifying glass. I have been greatly touched and encouraged by the kind response to my previous series, but it was a disappointment to find that people were not only interested in the art, but they were also interested in me. It is the habit that does it. The veil and the cloak and the long black robe have a fascination for those who may not realise that beneath them is a rather dull woman. But if looking at, instead of merely through the magnifying glass helps someone to see the art more truly, then it is not important. I look forward to the day when it will dawn upon everybody that they can have odysseys and Grand Tours and share the fruits of the world. The capacity to see, to open up the vision of reality that an artist offers, is innate in us all. The greatest reward I could have is to know that, despite my inadequacies, more and more people are coming to believe in their own powers of artistic appreciation.

Sister Wendy's Grand Tour by Sister Wendy Beckett

A Read the text opposite quickly. Is the writer:

a a professional TV presenter?
b a travel writer?
c an artist?
d a nun?

B Multiple-choice questions. Choose the best answer.

1 The main purpose of sending young men on a Grand Tour was to
   A prepare them for positions of power.
   B enable them to learn about democratic traditions.
   C develop their linguistic abilities.
   D keep them out of the country for a long period.

2 The writer says that many of the young men who went on Grand Tours
   A stayed away for longer than was necessary.
   B were criticized for improper behaviour.
   C failed to fulfil the aims of their journey.
   D were not properly supervised by their tutors.

3 It would appear that the money to pay for the writer's Grand Tour
   A came from a television company.
   B was given by the Carmelite sisters.
   C was provided from her savings.
   D was insufficient to provide reasonable standards of comfort.

4 The writer disliked being asked whether she was enjoying her tour because
   A she was forced to tell white lies.
   B it made her realize how much she wanted to be alone.
   C giving a frank answer made her appear unappreciative.
   D she felt guilty about deriving so much pleasure from it.

5 The writer says that the interest shown in her personally
   A detracted from what she was trying to achieve.
   B may in fact have helped some people appreciate art better.
   C has encouraged her to continue her work.
   D gave her greater self-confidence.

C Vocabulary. What is the meaning of the following words or phrases as they are used in the passage? Choose the best answer.

1 *very* (line 39)
   A a lot of   B previously referred to   C extremely

2 *bent on* (line 41)
   A not straight   B criminal   C intent on

3 *uncomplementary* (line 44)
   A mutually exclusive   B rude   C related

4 *absolutely* (line 76)
   A extremely   B objectively   C definitely

5 *touched* (line 86)
   A slightly mad   B handled   C affected emotionally

D Summary. In 40–60 words, summarize both the original motivation and the writer's motivation behind the Grand Tour.

Structure

Rewriting

For each of the sentences below, write a new sentence as similar as possible in meaning using the word given in CAPITALS. This word must not be altered in any way.

1 Her career took a different course when she was 30.

   TACK

   _____

2 Only Maria's mother is French.

   SIDE

   _____

3 Janet's husband can behave very aggressively at times.

   STREAK

   _____

4 The film star is staying in a specially designed caravan.

   PURPOSE

   _____

5 Because of the delay we missed our connecting flight.

   MEANT

   _____

6 The painter tried out a lot of different techniques.

   EXPERIMENTED

   _____

7 You have 30 days in which to complete and return this form.

   WITHIN

   _____

8 A number of younger artists value old customs and traditions.

   SEE

Gradable and ungradable adjectives

A Read the following letter and choose the best option, A, B, C or D, for 1–15.

Dear Laura,

I can't tell you how much I am enjoying my course in Florence; it's an absolutely 1 _____ place to study art history, and the thought that I will be here for another three months is 2 _____ marvellous.

Everything in the city is a feast for the eyes, and I am not only talking about the galleries. Everyone seems to dress 3 _____ well – the Italians seem to be totally 4 _____ fashion and they must spend a(n) 5 _____ fortune on clothes. (Your average English person in his very 6 _____ clothes would look 7 _____ ridiculous and out of place here.) The shops have to be seen to be believed; they're 8 _____ expensive admittedly, but the displays are lovely. And so you can imagine, just sitting having a coffee in the Piazza del Duomo, in the shadow of the Baptistery with Ghiberti's magnificent doors, watching the world go by, is a 9 _____ stunning experience.

As far as the course is concerned, it's all going well. As you know, I was 10 _____ worried about my Italian, because I am 11 _____ aware of how bad it is, but in fact I've been 12 _____ fine. I am expected to speak it all the time of course, which is 13 _____ reasonable, and although they probably find my accent highly 14 _____, everyone has been 15 _____ polite.

Anyway, I have to go now as I've got a lecture on the Medicis.

Love to everyone,

Jane

1 A interesting B attractive C ideal D good

2 A just B terribly C incredibly D very

3 A totally B amazingly C utterly D absolutely

4 A interested in B keen on C fond of D obsessed with

5 A terrible B absolute C amazing D incredible

6 A ghastly B dreadful C appalling D dull

7 A terribly B very C utterly D amazingly

8 A just B absolutely C pretty D utterly

9 A highly B very C terribly D totally

10 A bitterly B fully C perfectly D seriously

11 A most B bitterly C deeply D fully

12 A absolutely B terribly C very D pretty

13 A highly B perfectly C fully D greatly

14 A funny B laughable C ridiculous D amusing

15 A most B fully C seriously D highly

B Practice. Reply to these questions briefly using a modifier and an adjective in your answer.

How would you feel if you ….

1 … discovered a large snake in your garden?

_____

2 … had the chance to travel round the world for a year?

_____

3 … found out that a supposedly good friend had been lying to you?

_____

4 … were accused of a serious crime you had not committed?

_____

5 … were alone in a new city?

_____

6 … had just got the job of your dreams?

_____

animalcrackers

gr   pr   h   sc   b   owl

A Combine the word *owl* with the letters above to make words which mean the following.

1 look angrily
2 cry dolefully
3 utter angrily
4 move stealthily
5 travel rapidly

Which word is pronounced differently from the others?

B Now use one of the words in its correct form and a suitable adverb from 1–5 to complete the sentences below.

a Some strange dog was _____ about outside our house last night.

b The lone wolf _____ at the full moon.

c The postman _____ as he walked up the garden path and saw the huge Alsatian dog.

d The cartoon character Roadrunner had legs which used to turn into wheels and the animal would _____ along.

e The Alsatian dog _____ at the postman who was delivering the letters.

Vocabulary review

Choose the word which best completes each sentence.

1 As part of the research project, we had to ___ a list of all the American words that were commonly used in French.
A elaborate B draw C compile D amass

2 The photo would have been wonderful had it not been ___ focus.
A beyond B far from C out of D without

3 When I got to the airport, I discovered to my ___ that I had left my passport at home.
A shock B horror C dread D terror

4 Most of Aesop's children's stories have a(n) ___ that is explained clearly at the end.
A duty B right C moral D ethic

5 The Minister objected strongly to the negative way in which he was ___ in the newspaper article.
A delineated B relayed C deployed D portrayed

6 The TV series *Eureka* aims to ___ science and to make it accessible to a wide audience.
A popularize B forward C promulgate D proclaim

7 I think that this painting can be ___ in a number of different but equally valid ways.
A translated B interpreted C rendered D discerned

8 You really shouldn't have ___ to so much trouble – a sandwich would have been fine for lunch.
A set B gone C caused D put

9 Although there's plenty of leg-room in the front of the car, the back is a bit ___.
A reduced B confined C restrained D cramped

10 It was very ___ of you not to discuss the problem with me first.
A ludicrous B ridiculous C foolish D absurd

11 When you come down the hill do drive slowly because it's not ___ obvious where the turning is.
A immediately B directly C instantaneously D quite

12 I thought the first *Powerman* film was excellent but I didn't think the ___ was nearly as good.
A consequence B sequel C follow-up D supplement

13 Taking a genuine personal interest in our students is the ___ of our school's success.
A sandstone B headstone C foundation stone
D cornerstone

14 I can never see my ex-girlfriend ___ thinking how things used to be between us.
A except for B apart from C unless D without

15 You really ought to go to bed – you look absolutely ___.
A weary B weak C tired D shattered

ONLY FLESH AND BLOOD

A Write a paragraph describing this photograph. Speculate on:
- the place
- the nationality of the people
- the historical period
- their jobs

B Now read this article, which is connected with the photograph.

Jonathan Raban, *The Guardian Weekend*

Heartbreak in the heartland

From the spring of 1907 through the fall of 1908, the Chicago, Milwaukee and St Paul
05 railroad line lumbered through the Dakotas and into Montana. From the top of any hill, one could have seen its course
10 through the badlands: the lines of horse-drawn wagons, the heaps of broken rock for the roadbed, the debris, the
15 gangs of labourers, engineers, surveyors. From a distance, the construction of the new line looked like a
20 battlefield.

As the line advanced, it flung infant cities into being every dozen miles or so. Trains needed to be
25 loaded with freight and passengers, and it was the essential business of the railroad company to furnish its territory with
30 customers to create instant communities of people whose lives would be dependent on the umbilical cord of the line.
35 The company said, 'Let there be a city', and there was a city.

Each was a duplicate of the last. Main Street was a
40 down-at-heel line of

boxes, wood and brick, laid out on the prairie, transverse to the railroad line. The boxes housed a
45 post office, a hotel, a saloon, a general store, a saddlery, a barbershop, a church, a bank, a schoolhouse and a jail.
50 Beside the line, sites were staked out for the grain elevator and the stockyard. A few dilapidated shacks, and
55 the shabby city was done. Photographed from the proper angle, with railroad workers for citizens, it could be promoted as the
60 coming place in the New West.

As the railroads pushed farther west, into open rangeland that grew
65 steadily drier and steadily emptier, the rival companies clubbed together to sponsor an extraordinary body of
70 popular literature. For the increasingly inhospitable land to be settled by the masses of people needed to sustain the advance of
75 the railroads, it had to be made palpable. Railroad writers and illustrators were assigned to come up with a new picture of free,
80 rich farmland – a picture so attractive that readers would commit their families and their life-savings to it, sight unseen.
85 Pamphlets were distributed by railroad agents all over the US and Europe. Every mass-circulation newspaper
90 carried exaggerated advertisements translated into many languages. They turned up in bars and barbershops, in
95 doctors' waiting rooms and train carriages.

They dangled before the reader the prospect of fantastic self-
100 improvement, of riches going begging for the want of claimants. The terms of the Enlarged Homestead Act, passed in
105 Congress in 1909, were

generous. The size of a government homestead on 'semi-arid' land, like that of Eastern Montana,
110 was doubled from a quarter-section to a half-section, 160 acres to 320 acres. It was an outstanding free offer by
115 any reckoning.

The homesteaders arrived in a run of moist years – 1910, 1911, 1912 – and the land, in its
120 heyday, was living up to its descriptions in the railroad pamphlets. Then the weather broke.

In 1916, the winter cold
125 gave the settlers the first taste of the pitiless, extreme character of the Montana climate. When stable, high-pressure Arctic
130 air settled in over the prairie, it brought blue-sky days without a cloud to insulate the earth at night. There was almost no
135 precipitation. With no shelter-belts of trees to divert it, the north wind raked the homesteads; whistling through every
140 crack in their amateur carpentry, prying off their tarpaper sidings. The temperature dropped, and went on dropping: past
150 zero, into the tens, twenties, thirties, forties. Then there was wind, fire, lightning and ice. Montana's violent climate
155 came with the territory. In 1917 barely five inches of rain fell between May and August, and the harvest was disappointingly thin.
160 Most people were baffled and frightened by the disastrous turn in the weather. They had been assured – by the
165 government, by scientists, by the railroad literature – that this couldn't happen.

Rain suddenly chose to come back to the prairie
170 in 1926. By this time, many of the destitute settlers had already abandoned their homesteads.

C Multiple-choice questions. Choose the best answer.

1 During 1907 and 1908, the Montana landscape looked as if it had been
   A devastated by fire.
   B inundated by storms.
   C ravaged by conflict.
   D plundered by bandits.

2 Why was the railroad company eager to set up cities?
   A to house the railroad workers
   B to create a demand for the railroad
   C to create markets for goods carried by the railroad
   D to provide affordable accommodation for settlers

3 What did the photographs of the cities show?
   A a community struggling to survive
   B enticing new developments
   C new citizens who had recently arrived there
   D empty sites on which houses could be built

4 The popular literature set out to persuade people
   A to come and work on the railroad.
   B to invest in a project they knew little about.
   C to find out more about life in mid-America.
   D to contribute articles about newly settled areas.

5 According to the writer, what did the Act passed by Congress in 1909 state?
   A There was plenty of land for anybody who wished to claim it.
   B Only those with practical skills would be considered as claimants.
   C Land would be distributed free of charge to the homeless from abroad.
   D Claimants would receive twice as much land as previously expected.

6 What happened to the settlers in the winter of 1916?
   A They had to insulate their homes against the cold.
   B They were unable to go out because of the cold.
   C They were subjected to extreme weather conditions.
   D They had to rebuild their homes after violent storms.

7 Which description best sums up the main point of the passage?
   A Innocent people had been tricked.
   B The railroad caused the destruction of the countryside.
   C Montana cities were places of austerity.
   D The riches of Montana were somewhat exaggerated.

D Comprehension. Explain these phrases in your own words and say what they refer to.

1 *it flung infant cities into being* (line 22)
2 *dependent on the umbilical cord of the line* (line 33)
3 *it had to be made palpable* (line 75)
4 *They dangled before the reader* (line 97)
5 *going begging for the want of claimants* (line 101)
6 *a run of moist years* (line 117)

E Summary. In about 80 words, summarize how the homesteaders were encouraged to go and settle in Montana.

Transformations

Finish each sentence in such a way that it means exactly the same as the one before it.

1 It was vital that they loaded the perishable cargo quickly.

The perishable cargo _____

_____

2 It appears that railroad agents distributed popular literature throughout the US and Europe.

Popular literature _____

_____

3 According to the literature, rich pickings awaited the settlers.

The settlers were led _____

_____

4 People thought that some homesteaders had already settled in Montana.

Some homesteaders _____

_____

5 The 1909 Act promised new settlers a large, free plot of land.

A large, free plot of land _____

_____

6 The government hastily disposed of the semi-arid land.

The semi-arid land _____

_____

7 It is said that westerners never recovered from this betrayal.

Westerners _____

_____

8 They say that in 1916 the temperature dropped to –40°C.

The temperature _____

_____

Rewriting

For each of the sentences below, write a new sentence as similar as possible in meaning using the word given in CAPITALS. This word must not be altered in any way.

1 I seem to offend people, however much I try not to!

HELP

_____

2 The venture has been a disaster but nothing can be done about it now.

HELPED

_____

3 Don't wait to be asked if you want a sandwich!

HELP

_____

4 Let me give you a hand with all this paperwork.

OUT

_____

5 The staff are always so obliging to customers in this store.

LEND

_____

6 The coffee is just about finished.

SHORT

_____

Blank-filling

Fill each of the blanks in the following sentences with a suitable word or phrase.

1 The railroad companies _____ best to attract new settlers to the area.

2 That new supervisor thinks he's so superior. He needs to _____ two.

3 I hope you won't take it _____ if I say something rather personal.

4 Despite her _____, I feel the new recruit will be a success.

5 Check your money to make sure you haven't been _____ the shopkeeper.

6 We wouldn't have missed the experience _____ world.

7 The flights are all full at the moment so you'll just have to _____ luck.

8 I'm afraid wearing jeans _____ upon in this restaurant.

Vocabulary review

Choose the word which best completes each sentence.

1 Some of the homesteads abandoned by the settlers are now ___ .
   A destitute   B dejected   C derelict

2 Reports of the damage caused by strong winds have been ___ .
   A exaggerated   B extravagant   C extortionate

3 Some birds in the northern hemisphere ___ to the southern hemisphere in winter.
   A immigrate   B migrate   C emigrate

4 The early settlers were completely ___ on the harvest to see them through the winter.
   A dependant   B depended   C dependent

5 There were no clouds to ___ the earth against the intense cold.
   A insulate   B isolate   C infiltrate

6 The settlers had been ___ that Montana would make them rich.
   A insured   B assured   C ensured

7 The company is looking for more staff as they are rather ___ at the moment.
   A short-listed   B short-changed   C short-handed

8 ___ to the weather forecast, temperatures will drop to –20°C tonight.
   A Related   B According   C Subject

9 I caught a ___ of the aeroplane as it disappeared into the clouds.
   A glance   B glimpse   C gaze

10 The extreme weather conditions ___ their toll on the inhabitants.
   A assumed   B judged   C took

Vocabulary

animalcrackers

A Put these words into the four columns below, according to how the letters *rat* are pronounced.

migrate   infiltrate

congratulate   generate

rationalize

reiterate   ingratiate

fraternize   concentrate

perpetrate

WELL DONE

/ae/	/ei/	/aeʃ/	/eiʃ/

B Now match the words with these meanings.

1 try to gain somebody's favour
2 befriend those from different groups or races
3 enter secretly
4 try to explain or understand one's actions
5 commit (a crime)
6 express pleasure at someone's achievements
7 repeat something that has already been said
8 move from one place to another
9 give one's full attention to
10 produce

Fill each of the numbered blanks in the article with <u>one</u> suitable word.

In 1994, on the 25th anniversary of the Apollo moon-landing, the Washington Post published the intriguing ___1___ of a recent poll: 20 million Americans appear to have believed that the moon-landing was a hoax, perpetrated in the Arizona desert by the US government ___2___ the financial benefit of the big corporations who were the NASA contractors. A side-finding was that westerners were twice as ___3___ as easterners to subscribe to this conspiracy theory, which was a fine example of how gnarled scepticism, carried ___4___ enough, eventually turns ___5___ innocent credulity.

Yet, if one ___6___ to look for evidence to support the idea ___7___ the federal government was into scams of this magnitude, one has ___8___ to remember the dryland homestead scheme. In 1909, the government ___9___ drop people on to an expanse of land which looked suspiciously ___10___ to the surface of the moon. The scheme had been pushed ___11___ by Congress largely for the benefit of the railroad companies. If people in the west now showed a disproportionate mistrust ___12___ government and big corporations, they had in their history one event, at ___13___, that they could hold up in triumphant proof of their cynical imaginings.

Did the government know that, ___14___ the long term, the free land was unfarmable and that the scheme ___15___ end in heartbreak? They ___16___ well have done, but I very ___17___ doubt it. There was, however, real mendacity in the way the scheme ___18___ into being. The copywriters and art editors created a paper-country. The misleading language and pictures of the pamphlets would eventually entitle the homesteaders to see ___19___ as innocent dupes of a government that was in the pocket of the corporation fat cats – and their sense of ___20___ been betrayed would fester through the generations.

WORDS SPEAK VOLUMES

Cloze

A Copy out the following sentence in your normal handwriting.

Donald Duck dined in Denver on Thursday.

_____

B Now fill each of the numbered blanks in this text with <u>one</u> suitable word.

An interesting aspect of graphic symbolism is the extent to which individual variations in letter formation can reliably be interpreted. The term graphology, which 1_____ to the psychological study of handwriting, has been practised for 2_____ a century. 3_____ was the French abbot, Jean Hippolyte Michon (1806–81), who first 4_____ this branch of scholarship in train. Graphologists claim that careful and detailed 5_____ of an individual's handwriting can 6_____ important information about an individual's character and personality and can indicate, for example, 7_____ they are suitable for a particular job or not. In recent years they have been employed in several professional contexts and in forensic science, 8_____ questions of handwriting identity and imitation (i.e. forgery) are critical.

The subject plainly has the 9_____ for scientific development, as variables 10_____ as letter size, shape, angle, line direction and consistency of stroke all 11_____ themselves, 12_____ principle, to precise scientific description. Graphology has however suffered from scepticism generated by its popularity at agricultural shows and seaside resorts, where characters are described and 13_____ foretold on the 14_____ of little more than a scribbled signature. The subject has also been heavily biased 15_____ the famous or infamous, discerning the basis of success in a signature – but 16_____ objective controls.

The field can do much better than this, and the goal that current researchers have set 17_____ is to develop a full description of the handwriting practices of the general 18_____ under much more controlled conditions. To this 19_____ they have started using electronic resources such as computational techniques of magnification and pattern matching which have hardly been used up to 20_____.

C Handwriting analysis. Read through the following information about how to interpret handwriting by examining variations of the letter 'd'. Analyse the sentence you wrote above (Donald Duck dined in Denver on Thursday) in the light of this information, and find three or four features that refer to you.

When you are in class again, you can analyse each other's sentences and see if you agree.

1 Open at bottom
Wants to know himself

2 Left parts tastelessly exaggerated
Vulgarity

3 Written in two parts
Individualism, lack of adjustment

4 Second arc broad, with extended stroke
Underlining of own importance

5 Block letter
Simplification, intelligence

6 With claw to left
Egoist

7 Stroke extended at top
Enterprise

8 Upper length extended
Respect for spiritual values, integrity

9 Open at top and broad, or in two parts
Talkativeness

10 Simplified with arc to left
Taste

11 In form of musical notes or keys
Musicality

12 Open at bottom
Hypocrisy

13 Stroke to the right
Defensiveness

14 Enrolled
Secretiveness, family man or woman

15 Loops
Vanity

16 Filled with ink
Sensuality

Structure

Transformations

Finish each sentence in such a way that it means exactly the same as the one before it.

1 I'm worried about Jason because he just watches TV all day.

I'm worried about Jason because all _____

_____

2 It's why you want to live in Africa at all that I can't understand.

What _____

_____

3 Picasso painted *Guernica,* not Dali.

It _____

_____

4 Harriet was upset because she saw Peter with another woman.

It _____

_____

5 I really don't think it's my fault that the TV blew up. I just turned it on, that's all.

I really don't think it's my fault that the TV blew up. All

_____

_____

6 Not until the body was found did the police believe her.

It was only _____

_____

7 He broke the window because there was no other way of getting into the house.

There was no way of getting into the house, so what

_____

_____

8 1914 was the year when the First World War began.

It _____

_____

Vocabulary

Making opposites

A Form negative adjectives beginning with *in-, ir-, il-* or *im-,* using the base forms below.
- *appropriacy* • *cease* • *cohere* • *delete*
- *mutation* • *plausibility* • *revere* • *logic*

B Now complete the following sentences with a suitable negative adjective from those above.

1 The bank's _____ demands for repayment nearly gave Mr Wilkes a nervous breakdown.

2 The excuse he gave for being late, which involved a story about being held up by bank robbers, sounded highly

_____.

3 As the disease progressed, his speech degenerated from being difficult to understand to being completely

_____.

4 Stoppard's latest play is a masterpiece of wit, full of biting satire and _____ humour.

5 It is _____ to assume that Berenice is a marvellous cook just because she is French.

6 Energy can neither be created nor destroyed – that is one of the _____ laws of physics.

7 I felt that turning up at the wedding in jeans and a T-shirt was rather _____.

8 Please ensure that your child's sports clothes are clearly marked in _____ ink.

C Think of a word beginning with one of the above prefixes which means:

1 against the law
2 not prejudiced
3 unable to read
4 wrong
5 not reasonable
6 not to the point
7 lacking feeling for other people
8 able to live forever

Reading and Summary

A Read the following text.

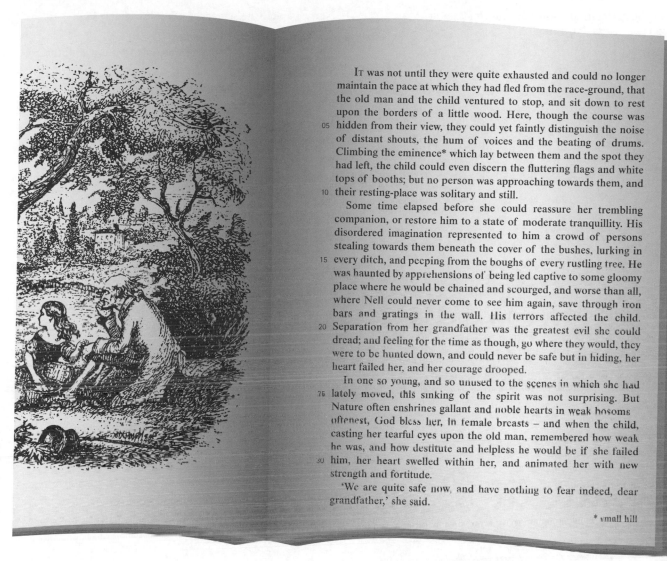

The Old Curiosity Shop by Charles Dickens

Iᴛ was not until they were quite exhausted and could no longer maintain the pace at which they had fled from the race-ground, that the old man and the child ventured to stop, and sit down to rest upon the borders of a little wood. Here, though the course was
05 hidden from their view, they could yet faintly distinguish the noise of distant shouts, the hum of voices and the beating of drums. Climbing the eminence* which lay between them and the spot they had left, the child could even discern the fluttering flags and white tops of booths; but no person was approaching towards them, and
10 their resting-place was solitary and still.

Some time elapsed before she could reassure her trembling companion, or restore him to a state of moderate tranquillity. His disordered imagination represented to him a crowd of persons stealing towards them beneath the cover of the bushes, lurking in
15 every ditch, and peeping from the boughs of every rustling tree. He was haunted by apprehensions of being led captive to some gloomy place where he would be chained and scourged, and worse than all, where Nell could never come to see him again, save through iron bars and gratings in the wall. His terrors affected the child.
20 Separation from her grandfather was the greatest evil she could dread; and feeling for the time as though, go where they would, they were to be hunted down, and could never be safe but in hiding, her heart failed her, and her courage drooped.

In one so young, and so unused to the scenes in which she had
25 lately moved, this sinking of the spirit was not surprising. But Nature often enshrines gallant and noble hearts in weak bosoms oftenest, God bless her, in female breasts – and when the child, casting her tearful eyes upon the old man, remembered how weak he was, and how destitute and helpless he would be if she failed
30 him, her heart swelled within her, and animated her with new strength and fortitude.

'We are quite safe now, and have nothing to fear indeed, dear grandfather,' she said.

* small hill

B Multiple-choice questions. Choose the best answer.

1 The old man and the child stopped when they
A had got out of the wood.
B were too tired to continue.
C felt it was safe to do so.
D had found a suitable place to hide.

2 The child climbed to a place where she could
A be seen from the race-course.
B hear what her pursuers were saying.
C see clearly what was happening at the race-course.
D see that they were not being followed.

3 The old man was in such a state of shock
A that it was difficult for the child to calm him down.
B that he imagined that he had been thrown into prison.
C because the wood was full of dangerous people.
D that he imagined he was surrounded by thieves.

4 The child began to feel a sense of despair because she
A could not bear to see her grandfather in such a condition.
B dreaded the thought of being separated from her grandfather.
C realized that they would never be safe.
D was frightened of being sent to prison.

5 The child told her grandfather there was nothing to fear
A because she needed his support.
B even though she did not believe it.
C because she was confident that no one was following them.
D because she was too young to realize how dangerous their situation was.

C Summary. In 40–60 words, summarize the fears of both the grandfather and the granddaughter.

Idioms

A Look at the cartoons and work out which idiom or expression each one is illustrating.

B Now complete the sentences using the idioms in A.

a The convict managed to get hold of a _____, so he was able to unlock all the doors and escape.

b She got caught in the rain and when she arrived at the office she _____.

c Jean-Pierre is so fluent in English that you might think it was his _____.

d When Harvey left prison he was determined to _____, and promised himself that he would earn an honest living.

e I don't trust your lawyer – I think he's trying to _____ because he's got something to hide.

f I waved my hands at the teacher because I wanted _____.

g I find Melissa very arrogant and I hate the way she _____ at everyone.

h If the tax people find out what you've been up to, they will _____.

C Now write five sentences of your own showing the meaning of the following idioms.

1 to be word perfect

_____

_____

2 to read between the lines

_____

_____

3 to take something as read

_____

_____

4 to be lost for words

_____

_____

5 word for word

_____

_____

Vocabulary review

Choose the word which best completes each sentence.

1 He is a successful politician, but he has achieved his goals at the _____ of his colleagues.
A detriment B sacrifice C expense D mercy

2 The examiner noted that there were _____ similarities between a number of compositions.
A knocking B hitting C slapping D striking

3 Through painstaking investigations, the police have been able to _____ the events of the night of the crime.
A reconstruct B rebuild C restore D reassemble

4 Tonight's episode of *Culture and Nature* gives a unique _____ into the lives of tribespeople in the Amazon rainforest.
A view B aspect C insight D spotlight

5 Fortunately the witness had a good look at the burglar and was able to give the police a _____ description.
A total B close C full D whole

6 I found the prospect of reading the 900-page book rather _____ .
A overbearing B strenuous C forbidding D daunting

7 Motivation and parental support are two of the _____ features of learning to read successfully.
A solution B key C answer D discovery

8 The latest food scare was _____ by revelations that a number of people were being treated for severe food poisoning.
A encouraged B developed C prompted D assisted

9 Although it is not widespread, Chinese has the largest number of _____ speakers.
A natural B mother C native D local

10 The company is launching a new advertising campaign to _____ new customers to its stores.
A appeal B attract C interest D fascinate

11 _____ Japanese is certainly complex, it is by no means impossible to learn.
A While B Whereas C Since D However

12 _____ English, which has no gender system, German has masculine, feminine and neuter.
A Besides B Except C Apart D Unlike

13 _____ French was the international language of commerce and diplomacy in the 18th century, English has become the lingua franca of the modern world.
A At first glance B Despite C However D Just as

14 Malay has a remarkably simple tense structure, _____ English has a lot of different tenses.
A whereas B however C despite D unlike

15 _____ , free health care is an attractive idea, but it has a number of serious drawbacks and practical problems.
A Because B At first glance C Despite D Just as

Vocabulary

animalcrackers

A Strange combinations Combine the animals in the box with the words to the left of them to make phrases which mean the following:

1 someone who starts work earlier than others
2 an active person who moves quickly from task to task
3 someone who prefers his or her own company
4 a person or object in a vulnerable position which is easy to attack or injure
5 someone who is regarded as being hard or unfeeling
6 a voracious reader
7 someone who is often quiet or has greater abilities than he or she shows
8 a very slow speed

a dark _____ a sitting _____

a book _____ a busy _____

a lone _____ an early _____

a _____'s pace a cold _____

B Choose four of the phrases above and use them in sentences of your own.

Writing

Metamorphosis

A These descriptions of the life cycle of a frog are in the wrong order. Arrange them to correspond with the three stages of a frog's development.

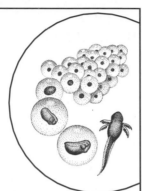

leaving the water

breeding

gulping air from the surface of the water

climbing trees

developing lungs

breathing through gills

feeding on yolks inside jelly

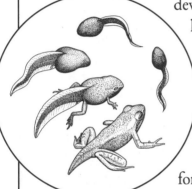

forming limbs

hibernating in winter in northern countries

hopping

swimming with the aid of a long tail

hatching

losing their long tail

1 frog-spawn

2 tadpole

3 adult frog

B Now write a short paragraph outlining the three stages of development in the life cycle of a frog.

Reading

A Read the article. Then answer the questions below, using your own words as far as possible.

1 According to the SRI, what is the most important factor in the preservation of wildlife?

2 What effects has the change in land use had?

3 What was the main objective of the expedition?

4 What had the team not expected to find?

5 How did the local people react to the unusual group of people?

B Reference devices. What do the underlined words refer to in the article?

1 *This change in land use* (line 20)
2 *Unless their support can be won,* (line 33)
3 *With all this in mind,* (line 36)
4 *who live on its boundary* (line 54)
5 *by the sheer resilience of these communities* (line 66)
6 *a healthy respect for these offenders* (line 72)

C Vocabulary. The words on the left in **a–h** below appear in the article. Choose one of the words in each pair in its correct form to complete sentences 1–8.

a	ensure	assure
b	species	specimens
c	habitats	inhabitants
d	degradation	degeneration
e	effects	affects
f	resilience	resistance
g	adapt	adopt
h	consternation	consolation

1 The plan to inject investment capital into the region met with some _____.

2 The members of the expedition were _____ that they were physically capable of climbing Kilimanjaro.

3 The fact that the red squirrel has not completely disappeared from its traditional surroundings is some _____ for nature lovers.

4 Animal lovers can help wildlife by _____ an animal such as a whale or dolphin.

5 The conference has been called to discuss the _____ of tourism on the wildlife in the area.

6 There were some interesting _____ of dinosaur bones in the museum.

7 The _____ of the old man's mental faculties became more and more apparent as time went by.

8 Hedgerows and copses provide rich _____ for wildlife.

whose wildlife is it anyway?

As one of the leading campaigners for conservation, Save the Rhino (SRI) has recognised the fact that to ensure a long-term future for endangered
05 species, a greater emphasis must be placed on local communities who share the same environment that the wildlife inhabits.

It must be remembered that
10 national parks and reserves make up a minute percentage of Africa's land mass and it is not surprising that 80% of wild animals in Africa roam outside these areas amongst local people.
15 Rapidly expanding human populations combined with pressures to practise conventional agriculture have meant that rural communities have turned wild habitats into ploughed croplands.
20 This change in land use has played havoc with areas located around national parks and, in some cases, has led to environmental degradation, social decline, poverty and starvation
25 amongst local communities who live with wildlife on their doorsteps.

For over twenty years, the majority of international conservation efforts to protect endangered species like the
30 rhino, elephant and more recently the tiger, have neglected to involve the real guardians of wildlife – the local people. Unless their support can be won, wildlife has little chance of
35 survival in its natural state.

With all this in mind, SRI decided to put together a unique fund-raising concept which would highlight the people–wildlife conflict in areas of
40 Kenya and Tanzania. The ingredients of the expedition were eight walkers and a thirty pound, eight-foot-high rubber rhino costume. Our challenge was to see if we could walk the
45 (costume) rhino, in turns, from Mombasa at sea level to the top of Mount Kilimanjaro, Africa's highest

point. The expedition would last for a month and cover 300 kilometres to
50 the base of the mountain before climbing 5950 metres.

The walk passed alongside Tsavo game park. Rural communities who live on its boundary have rarely seen
55 the positive effects of wildlife and one of the primary objectives of our expedition was to identify the negative impact wildlife had on its human neighbours and find out why
60 there is a lack of emotional ownership amongst local people in regard to the

wildlife. Half-expecting to come up against disgruntled farmers and uninterested villagers, we were
65 pleasantly surprised and filled with hope by the sheer resilience of these communities who have, over the years, learned to adapt to the current situation. Wild animals, particularly
70 the buffalo and the elephant, are destroying their crops, yet there is still a healthy respect for these offenders.

The walk itself was going to be tough but by the third day we had
75 acclimatised and the average twenty-five kilometre walk could be covered in a morning. The (costume) rhino was, as one might expect, the highlight of this strange walking
80 entourage and even though the local people kept a safe distance, the crowds that gathered behind us to join the walk were proof that we had captured their interest. Up and down
85 the road people talked excitedly about the two-legged rhino which was walking to Kilimanjaro.

We spent a lot of time visiting primary schools which were situated
90 in the wildlife problem areas. The arrival of the rhino at these schools caused great consternation amongst the children and their parents but the welcomes we received were
95 unforgettable.

David Stirling, Msafiri, Kenya Airways In Flight Magazine

Blank-filling

Fill each of the blanks in the following sentences with a suitable word or phrase.

1 The bad weather played _____ with flight departures.

2 We have had no time to prepare for this committee meeting so we'll just have to play _____ to begin with.

3 The police suspected _____ play after the suspicious death of the bank manager.

4 The tiger is on _____ of extinction.

5 We should be _____ send us some information about *Save The Rhino*.

6 Martin has taken to climbing like _____ water.

7 Peter never listens to any advice you give him: it's like _____ back.

8 Sam is a big _____ pond in our company.

9 There is a _____ export of ivory from some countries.

10 If only he _____ a promise he knew he could never keep!

Transformations

Finish each sentence in such a way that it means exactly the same as the one before it.

1 In case of emergency, break the glass and sound the alarm.

Should _____

_____

2 Supposing I got the job abroad, would you come with me?

If I were _____

_____

3 The livestock had not been brought in for the night and many animals perished.

Had _____

_____

4 We must take steps to preserve natural resources, otherwise the planet will be in danger.

Unless _____

_____

5 Booking that camping holiday was a big mistake on our part.

If only _____

_____

6 The government can't be considering raising taxes immediately because they have only just lowered them!

If _____

_____

7 Sally is very disorganized so she has no chance of getting that secretarial job.

Were it _____

_____

8 The road was water-logged so we were unable to move our vehicle.

If it hadn't _____

_____

Cloze development

A Read this continuation of the article on page 47. The underlined words are wrong. Can you correct them?

Alike ⟦1⟧ our visits to the primary schools, our walk through Tsavo West park towards the border town of Taveta was a very alone ⟦2⟧ one and we turned our attention to the mountain ahead. Mount Kilimanjaro has to be one of the most awe-inspiring signs ⟦3⟧ you can see in Africa. Its snow-capped summit, raising ⟦4⟧ out of the blanket of cloud that envelopes it, sends adrenaline pumping fast round your body. The short rains had reached ⟦5⟧ late and, despite the fact that we welcomed them for the sake of the farmers, we were hoping that they might stay away other ⟦6⟧ week while we climbed the mountain. Mount Kilimanjaro is the highest free-standing mountain in the world and, however ⟦7⟧ we were concerned, there was a silent confidence amongst the team at this staging ⟦8⟧, as we all felt that we had the ability to reach the summit whenever ⟦9⟧ the weather. We were lucky, because ⟦10⟧ it turned out, for the sun shone on us almost any ⟦11⟧ day of the ascent and in the afternoon of the sixth day we all successfully reached Uhuru peak at 5950 metres. As we commemorated ⟦12⟧ our feat on the roof top of Africa, there was also time to reflect on what we had learned since ⟦13⟧ the past four weeks. People need to be put back into the picture whether ⟦14⟧ we are to find a place for wildlife in their vast rural holdings. Once that happens, once rural communities get more from wildlife than they loose ⟦15⟧, the prospects for the subsistence ⟦16⟧ of endangered species like the rhino brighten considerably.

B Summary. Based on information given in the article on page 47 and the continuation above, summarize in about 60 words the attitudes of local communities to wildlife. Link your information with suitable words and expressions.

---

animalcrackers

Vocabulary

A Arrange these words in three columns, according to how the letters *cat* are pronounced.

scattered   categorical   catastrophic   located   desiccated

cataclysmic   catastrophe   vocational

delicate   catty   catalogued

/ ae /	/ ei /	/ ə /

B Match each word to its meaning below. Two words are very similar in meaning.

1 situated
2 dispersed
3 malicious
4 unconditional
5 relating to employment

6 fragile
7 with the moisture removed
8 disastrous
9 listed
10 disaster

Vocabulary

Lost consonants

A In each sentence there is a word with a 'lost consonant'. Find the words and supply the missing consonants.

EXAMPLE

I returned to Kenya with the money we had raised to start the <u>wok</u> at five primary schools. *work*

1 For some people, sending money on holidays is one of life's pleasures.

2 I don't share their enthusiasm, and arrived in Nairobi with fir intentions of delegating as soon as possible.

3 When I met Michael Werikhe, he was eager to take pat in the project.

4 Werikhe is not a man to hag around when a job needs doing.

5 A day later we had a builder who was prepared to work on promoting wildlife projects in the right kid of environment.

6 Work on the classrooms was ready to star.

7 I was convinced that this fist attempt at involving the local community would be successful.

8 I hoped that work on all the classrooms would be competed in time for the summer term.

B Write five sentences, each with a 'lost consonant'. In your next class, see if a partner can correct them.

Writing

Project Tiger

These notes about tigers can be arranged into three different topic areas to form three paragraphs. The first paragraph has been done as an example. Arrange the remaining notes into two different topic areas and join them together in a suitable way to write paragraphs 2 and 3.

The tiger is a member of the cat family.
Tigers rest for most of the day.
The Latin name for the tiger is Panthera Tigris.
Tigers like to swim and when it is hot they often lie in water to keep cool.
Most cats do not like to swim.
Tigers are an endangered species.
Tigers usually start hunting late in the afternoon.
Tigers have always been extremely adaptable.
There are fewer than 6,000 tigers in the wild.
The main threat today comes from poachers.
Their striped coats give the perfect camouflage in forests and grasslands.
They prefer to hunt by ambushing passing animals.

They have very little endurance.
They kill tigers for their bones.
They occasionally hunt as a pair.
Tigers' bones are used in traditional Chinese medicine.
They have been able to live in a wide variety of climatic zones.
The other danger comes from the destruction of the forests.
They are unable to hunt in open country.
Tigers depend on forests for their survival.
They can be found in the winter snows of Siberia.
The forests are being destroyed by the human population.
The human population need to use the forests for agriculture.
They usually hunt alone.
Tigers are excellent swimmers.
The destruction of tiger habitats may continue.
They can be found in the tropical jungles of Malaysia, Thailand and other countries of Southeast Asia.
Tigers may become extinct.
An adult tiger will eat 18–27 kg of meat at one feed.

Introduction

The tiger, (Panthera Tigris), is a member of the cat family. Tigers have always been extremely adaptable, and have been able to live in a wide variety of climatic zones, ranging from the winter snows of Siberia to the tropical jungles of Malaysia, Thailand and other countries of Southeast Asia.

10

THE TIES THAT BIND

Read this text and fill each of the numbered blanks with <u>one</u> suitable word.

Psychologists agree that conflicts are inevitable in any long-term relationship. However, what matters most is the way in which they are resolved 1 _____ than the source of 2 _____ given conflict itself. 3 _____ to recent psychological studies, the methods couples use to settle their differences are crucial to the 4 _____ or failure of a relationship.

Although excessively aggressive behaviour patterns are undesirable, 5 _____ must be avoided at 6 _____ costs is the suppression of anger. Simply 7 _____ nothing about a problem is not a viable option; it 8 _____ to feelings of bitterness and resentment, which in turn can 9 _____ a relationship to break down irretrievably. Indeed there are some psychologists who believe that 10 _____ is this inability to deal with conflicts that accounts 11 _____ a large proportion of the ever-increasing cases of divorce.

It is essential for couples to communicate when things start going wrong, and this 12 _____ to almost any couple, 13 _____ long the relationship may have been 14 _____ on. The most successful method of resolving differences involves a three-stage process. Firstly, one partner should tell the other precisely what the problem is and should try to be positive rather than negative 15 _____ as not to create any additional tension. 16 _____ the couple should discuss the specific problem in detail, taking care not to rake up old grievances. 17 _____ and perhaps most importantly, there should be negotiation until an agreement is 18 _____. This does not necessarily mean that the problem will be 19 _____ and a couple may eventually only agree to disagree, but even this is 20 _____ to allowing a conflict to rankle.

Vocabulary

animal**crackers**

A Fill in the missing letters in 1–6 to make words which mean the same as those on the right.

1 ape __   summit

2 ape __ __ __ __ __   opening

3 __ __ ape   open-mouthed

4 ape __ __ __ __ __   a pre-dinner drink

5 __ __ ape   curtain

6 __ ape   headland or promontory

B In which words are the letters *ape* pronounced differently?

C Now use the words in sentences of your own.

Reading and Summary

A Read the following passage quickly and say whether statements 1–5 are true or false.

	T	F
1 The 'Wild Boy of Aveyron' was human.		
2 He lived in the forest with his mother and father.		
3 He was not happy after he had been captured.		
4 He occasionally behaved in very unusual ways.		
5 Eventually he made a lot of friends with children his own age.		

Not many years after the French philosopher Rousseau promulgated the idea of the 'noble savage', which embodied his belief that man in his
05 natural state, unsullied by civilization or education, was innately good, there walked out of the woods a living specimen who, it was hoped, would prove the point. It happened at the village of Saint-Sernin in southern France
10 on January 9, 1800. A strange creature from the forest was caught scavenging for food, and though it appeared to be a wild animal, it walked erect. As soon as those who captured the creature realized it was human, a boy of about
15 twelve years in fact, they attempted to care for him.

The 'Wild Boy of Aveyron', as he became known, had been in the forest for six years. He was virtually naked and very dirty, with no
20 apparent awareness that he was human, no modesty, and no ability to relate in any way to his captors. He could not speak and was intolerant of confinement. When his rescuers tried to clothe him, he tore the garments off and
25 ripped them to pieces. Offered white bread, he spat it out immediately, and seemed familiar only with potatoes. He bit anyone who approached too close. It was time to alert the scientists. Here, apparently, was the noble
30 savage in person.

Over the next few months, attempts were made to bring the boy back into the human race. (When he was found he wore the remnants of a tattered shirt, which indicated that he had
35 been lost or abandoned some years before.) He had the benefit of a patient tutor and a woman who grew to love him with a mother's devotion, yet he never learned to speak or return affection. With some optimism, he was given
40 the name Victor, but the experiments to which this poor wretch was subjected met with repeated defeat, while he longed to return to his freedom and his woods. His only pleasure was sipping a slow glass of water as he stared
45 through the imprisoning window at the sky and the moon, erstwhile companions of his solitary life. He did not, could not, understand civilization.

Most importantly, did Victor bring from his
50 natural state of innocence an inherent goodness which would put his civilized captors to shame? Invited to dinner at the salon of Madame Récamier, he stole everything small enough to grab and clambered up a tree, which left the
55 astonished guests resentful that Rousseau was not alive to see his theories disproved. But were they disproved? Theft is a transgression against a specific moral rule, but does not, in itself, denote badness if the rule has no significance
60 for the thief. What was infinitely more telling was the fact that Victor was never able to see the world through the eyes of anyone but himself and had no capacity for empathy. He certainly learned how people could hurt, for his
65 tutor, having bestowed love, would unwarrantably remove it to see how the boy reacted, which was, of course, with terrified disappointment. But he never learned to recognize that other people existed except as
70 satisfiers of his needs. The Wild Boy of Aveyron did not prove that the primitive state was one of essential goodness, but he did prove that it was irremediably selfish or self-centred. Which is not to say that it was not also innocent (literally
75 harmless): the boy showed no malice or cruelty, did not seek revenge, did not direct hostility against individuals. He was not so much immoral as pre-moral.

The Evil That Men Do by Brian Masters

B Multiple-choice questions. Read the text again carefully and choose the best answer.

1 When the Wild Boy was first found, he
  A had broken into a house to steal food.
  B was mistaken for an animal.
  C had been alone in the forest for twelve years.
  D demonstrated that Rousseau's theories had been correct.

2 The boy's captors handed him over to the scientists because
  A it was thought he would be of considerable interest to them.
  B they feared he might be a cannibal.
  C they were unsure of what to give him to eat.
  D he needed to be taught to speak.

3 The writer implies that the name Victor
  A was chosen because he had managed to survive alone for so long.
  B reflected the hopes and aspirations of his carers.
  C matched his physical strength.
  D was inappropriate because the boy had lost his freedom.

4 The writer suggests that the boy's behaviour at dinner
  A demonstrated that moral codes are not inborn.
  B showed that he was dishonest.
  C indicated that he wanted to return to the forest.
  D proved that the theories of Rousseau were wrong.

5 What interests and surprises the writer most about Victor's character is that he
  A was unable to distinguish right from wrong.
  B had no feelings.
  C had no capacity whatsoever for understanding other people.
  D was a thief.

6 The story of the Wild Boy of Aveyron would appear to indicate that man, in his primitive state, is innately
  A aggressive.
  B dishonest.
  C egocentric.
  D good.

C Vocabulary. Choose the closest meaning from the options A–C for these words as they are used in the passage.

1 *promulgated* (line 2)
  A proposed   B dismissed   C argued against

2 *unsullied by* (line 5)
  A not spoiled by   B unaffected by   C not interested in

3 *was intolerant of* (line 23)
  A was impatient with   B greatly disliked
  C misunderstood

4 *alert* (line 28)
  A awake   B warn   C inform

5 *tattered* (line 34)
  A torn   B creased   C dirty

6 *erstwhile* (line 46)
  A forgotten   B only   C former

7 *inherent* (line 50)
  A innate   B alternative   C hidden

8 *telling* (line 60)
  A significant   B amusing   C upsetting

9 *unwarrantably* (line 66)
  A illegally   B unjustifiably   C occasionally

10 *recognize* (line 69)
  A remember   B realize   C identify

D Summary. In 60–80 words, summarize the experiments the young boy was subjected to and their effects.

E Imagine you are abandoned on an uninhabited planet. Write about:

1 Your feelings and experiences in the first month.

2 Your lifestyle three years later.

3 Your first month back in civilization after having been rescued ten years later.

SAVAGE OF AVEYRON.

Structure

Tense and context

Join the sentences on the left with the most appropriate sentence on the right. The first one is done as an example.

1 I've been painting the dining room …

2 I've painted the dining room …

3 Yes, I've been reading *War and Peace* …

4 Yes, I've read *War and Peace* …

5 It's been snowing heavily in Scotland …

6 It has snowed heavily in Scotland …

7 Emma has been writing to Peter…

8 Emma has written to Peter…

9 My parents have been living in London …

10 My parents have lived in London

11 I've been running …

12 I've run …

a and he'll probably get the letter tomorrow.

b and I'm really enjoying it.

c all their lives.

d so driving conditions are hazardous.

e but they're moving to Bonn soon.

f almost every year since records began.

g so I suppose the next thing is the hall.

h but I can't remember what happens at the end.

i almost three miles today.

j but I'm too tired to finish it tonight.

k three times a week for most of this year, so I'm very fit.

l and he seems to get a letter almost every day.

1	2	3	4	5	6	7	8	9	10	11	12
j											

Tense review

Put each verb in brackets into the correct form of the appropriate tense. Use the present perfect simple/continuous, past perfect simple/continuous, or future perfect simple/continuous tense.

1 Henry's work _____ (improve) gradually since he started having private lessons, so we're going to continue with them.

2 The town centre _____ (change) completely over the last twenty years, and you would hardly recognize it.

3 The roads were very dangerous because _____ (snow) most of the morning.

4 Your father's a bit short-tempered at the moment because he _____ (work) very hard recently.

5 Do you realize that if the workmen are still there on Monday, they _____ (dig) up the road for a whole month?

6 I didn't know Claire was your girlfriend. How long _____ (you/go out) with each other?

7 By the time the war was over, thousands of innocent people _____ (kill).

8 I _____ (mean) to get the brakes repaired for ages, but I've just never got round to it.

9 If you don't hurry up, the party _____ (finish) by the time we get there.

10 It was obvious at once that the house _____ (break) into.

Rewriting

For each of the sentences below, write a new sentence as similar as possible in meaning using the word given in CAPITALS. This word must not be altered in any way.

1 His father's condition has deteriorated significantly.

SIGNIFICANT

_____

2 After the crash, there was debris all over the runway.

LITTERED

_____

3 I had to wait for ages until a bus arrived.

SPENT

_____

4 The Minister accepted that he was to blame for what had gone wrong.

FULL

_____

5 My mother was unsure whether my decision to become an actor was advisable.

MISGIVINGS

_____

6 I drove 200 miles to the concert, but then found I had gone on the wrong day.

ONLY

_____

7 Would you like to contribute something to our campaign?

MAKE

_____

8 I've got to eat less chocolate as part of my diet.

CUT

_____

Vocabulary review

Choose the word which best completes each sentence.

1 Police fear that an increasing number of young people in the city are becoming ___ to cocaine.
A obsessed B fixed C addicted D dependent

2 A man has been arrested as a result of a ___-off by an informer.
A tell B warn C tip D stand

3 He lost his job and his home and eventually ___ up living on the streets.
A reached B wound C set D went

4 It is ___ that the Minister of Justice should be accused of corruption.
A ironic B sarcastic C cynical D sardonic

5 Although they are often criticized in the press, single mothers ___ for only a very small proportion of government spending.
A cost B create C cause D account

6 You can't believe a word that woman says – she is a ___ liar.
A dedicated B devoted C committed D compulsive

7 There can be no ___ fixes or magic solutions to the problem of unemployment.
A fast B speedy C quick D sudden

8 When people drink alcohol, they tend to lose their ___.
A reserves B constraints C inhibitions D pressures

9 The power ___ lasted several days, and we had to throw out most of the food that was in the freezer.
A shortage B reduction C stoppage D cut

10 As the political situation ___, more and more people began to talk about the possibility of war.
A declined B worsened C descended D decreased

11 I didn't pay the electricity bill, so they sent me a ___.
A reminder B recollection C receipt D remittance

12 Many dentists concentrate on doing ___ work so that fillings never become necessary.
A precautionary B preventative C restorative
D defensive

13 How could you just abandon me in the middle of London with no money and leave me ___ and dry?
A cold B out C high D low

14 Mrs Marsh was ___ guilty of endangering the welfare of a child and sentenced to three months in prison.
A accused B condemned C found D convicted

15 The private detective looking for the missing teenager eventually ___ her down in London.
A followed B pursued C trailed D tracked

Writing

Varieties of English

Read the following extract from a letter, which is written in American English. Note down the changes you would make to turn it into British English. An example is given.

> I went to the theater last Thursday with Jane's brother, and we saw King Lear at Stratford. Unfortunately Jane couldn't come with us because she works Monday through Friday, and it means she's only free weekends. Anyway it was great, although while we were driving back we ran out of gas and had to be rescued by a patrolman, and by the time we'd gotten back to Jane's apartment it was nearly three in the morning! Jane was real mad with her brother when she heard about it, and said it was the dumbest thing she'd ever heard of.
>
> Well, I'd better go now. Jane just got back and we're going out for a drink with her mom. I'll call you Friday – I hope you don't mind if I make a collect call. Hope everything's OK with you, and don't forget to write me soon.
>
> Love,
> Laurie

EXAMPLE
I went to the theatre last Thursday ...

THE HARD SELL

A Read the following article.

CRAFTY PACKAGING

After reading this article, you'll never look at supermarket shelves in the same way again!

DURING a typical 30-minute shopping trip down the aisles of an average supermarket, thousands of products will vie for your attention. Ultimately, many will make you believe they are worth picking off the shelves. How? Packaging – the silent but persuasive salesman.

A pioneer in studying people's emotional response to packaging was Louis Cheskin, a specialist in the psychology of marketing who began his research in the 1930s. He placed identical products in two different packages, one emblazoned with circles, the other with triangles. Then he asked people which product they preferred, and why. More than 80 per cent chose the product in the box with the circles. They believed the content would be of higher quality.

'I found it difficult to believe the results after the first 200 interviews,' Cheskin admitted later. 'But after 1,000 interviews, I had to accept the fact that the majority of consumers transferred the sensation from the container to its contents.' And there was another surprise: even after <u>trying</u> these identical products, people overwhelmingly preferred those in the package with the circles.

Cheskin repeated the experiment for a wide variety of product types. He found, for instance, that the look of a packet has an enormous impact on how biscuits taste or how soaps are perceived to clean.

Cheskin called this phenomenon 'sensation transference'. It became the foundation not only of his career as a consultant to companies like Procter and Gamble and McDonald's, but of much of the research into package design that has been done since then.

Despite increasing consumer sophistication, Cheskin's original concept still works. One of the most dramatic versions of the Cheskin experiment involved an underarm deodorant posted in packaging of three different colour schemes to a test group. The group was told that three different formulations were under consideration, and was asked to judge them. Colour scheme B was considered just right. Scheme C was said to be strong-smelling but not very effective, and scheme A was deemed downright threatening. Several participants developed a skin rash after using it and had to consult dermatologists. Yet all three deodorants were exactly the same.

One leading package-designing firm, Primo Angeli of San Francisco, has carried this principle to a money-making extreme: the firm designs packaging for products that do not yet exist. The packaging is then tested and the marketing concept refined. Only when it's clear that the company has picked out a winner will it go to the expense of actually developing the product. A forthcoming product from Nestlé has been created this way.

The power of a packet may depend on a resolution of opposites – a conflict between the aggressiveness required for getting noticed in the supermarket and the need to appear soft and unaggressive when the packet is brought home. Triangles and other pointed figures attract notice. But as Cheskin's early experiment proved, just because people can see triangles, it doesn't mean they like them. And colour presents a different dilemma. Cheskin thought that the most noticeable hue was yellow, which for some products has negative connotations.

The process is certainly not rational.

To quote Stan Gross, a marketing consultant in Pennsylvania, 'I can't ask you why you like a certain package, and you can't tell me. The package is not silent. It screams – but it screams to your inner mind.' To plumb this inner mind, Gross asks groups of people to play games meant to elicit inner, pre-rational responses. Formed into teams, they are given a series of packets and challenged to tell stories about them. They are asked: 'If this toothpaste were a person, write its obituary.' Or, 'If this detergent were a film, what would it be about?' He encourages such playfulness because he thinks it bypasses rational judgement and gets truer reactions.

Obviously, Gross and other psychological marketers are dealing with fears and desires that go deeper than whiter laundry. Parents worry that they are failing their children. Individuals feel lonely and unfulfilled. To assuage these anxieties through such placebos as a frozen pizza or a packet of chewing gum – doesn't that seem cruel? Gross argues that people know, on some level, that the purchases they make will not fulfil their deepest wants. 'Buying things is a way of coping,' Gross says. We may know they are empty symbols, but we pursue these bright baubles because they satisfy us. And perhaps because, at still another level, we enjoy watching their gloriously sophisticated competition for our favours.

Thomas Hine

B Multiple-choice questions. Choose the best answer.

1 What did Cheskin's initial research show?
   A Customers who were offered free samples were more likely to make purchases.
   B Customers preferred to feel or taste products before deciding which was best.
   C Triangular shapes on packaging made less impact on customers than circles.
   D Packaging with circles and triangles persuaded more customers to make purchases.

2 The deodorant experiment showed that
   A demand cannot be created by the quality of a product alone.
   B different products can affect consumers in different ways.
   C products sold in several different packagings will sell more.
   D a product needs to be of good quality to be a continuing success.

3 What does the firm Primo Angeli specialize in?
   A financing the projects of smaller companies
   B marketing the products of larger companies
   C creating designer products for packaging companies
   D producing packaging for mythical products

4 What conflicting considerations do packaging designers have to bear in mind?
   A customer needs versus customer desires
   B competitive pricing versus good quality
   C dynamic impact versus non-threatening presence
   D eye-catching beauty versus long-term credibility

5 What is the real point of the 'playfulness' advocated by Gross?
   A It is a more introspective activity.
   B It achieves more reliable results.
   C It is more challenging for the participants.
   D It is less time-consuming than other methods.

6 What explanation is suggested for the reactions of customers to the carefully packaged products?
   A They believe the products are fulfilling their own secret desires.
   B They see the products as symbols of their own potential success.
   C They may appreciate the effort put into marketing the products.
   D They buy the products to satisfy their craving for spending.

C Vocabulary. Choose the word or phrase which is nearest in meaning to the words as they appear in the article.

1 *vie for* (line 4)
   A compete for   B demand   C attract

2 *emblazoned* (line 15)
   A draped   B adorned   C surrounded

3 *overwhelmingly* (line 31)
   A stunningly   B uncontrollably   C vastly

4 *impact* (line 36)
   A contact   B blow   C effect

5 *phenomenon* (line 39)
   A occurrence   B exception   C incident

6 *deemed* (line 61)
   A held   B estimated   C considered

7 *dilemma* (line 89)
   A mess   B problem   C embarrassment

8 *connotations* (line 93)
   A associations   B colourings   C nuances

9 *obituary* (line 109)
   A achievements   B job history   C notice of death

10 *assuage* (line 120)
   A soothe   B identify   C combat

11 *placebos* (line 121)
   A junk food   B substitutes   C panaceas

12 *baubles* (line 128)
   A trinkets   B toys   C niceties

D Homonyms. The following words appear in the article. Suggest at least one other meaning for each one. Use a dictionary, if necessary.

1 trip (line 2)	6 career (line 41)
2 box (line 19)	7 posted (line 51)
3 content (line 20)	8 rash (line 63)
4 types (line 34)	9 presents (line 89)
5 taste (line 37)	10 plumb (line 102)

E Reported speech. Punctuate the direct speech below. Then rewrite it as reported speech.

1 I found it difficult to believe the results after the first 200 interviews Cheskin admitted later but after 1,000 interviews I had to accept the fact that the majority of consumers transferred the sensation from the container to its contents

   Cheskin admitted _____

2 to quote Stan Gross a marketing consultant in Pennsylvania I cant ask you why you like a certain package and you cant tell me the package is not silent it screams but it screams to your inner mind

   Stan Gross, a marketing consultant in Pennsylvania, commented _____

3 they are asked if this toothpaste were a person write its obituary or if this detergent were a film what would it be about

   Gross asks people_____

4 buying things is a way of coping Gross says

   Gross _____

F Summary. In 60–80 words, summarize Stan Gross's theories about the influence of packaging on consumers. Link your information with suitable words and expressions.

Transformations

Finish each sentence in such a way that it means exactly the same as the one before it, using one of the verbs given.

- *boasted*   • *suggested*   • *conceded*   • *denied*
- *announced*   • *insisted*   • *accused*   • *warned*

1 'No, I had nothing whatsoever to do with the theft,' said the security guard.

The security guard _____

_____

2 'What about trying to buy more products in bulk?', said the Marketing Manager.

The Marketing Manager _____

_____

3 'Unless we improve our sales figures, the firm will go to the wall,' said the Sales Manager.

The Sales Manager _____

_____

4 'Zenco is the best packaging company in the country,' said the foreman.

The foreman _____

_____

5 'All right, the company is only just managing to break even,' said the accountant.

The accountant _____

_____

6 'I assure the board I have taken all aspects of the company's performance into consideration,' said the consultant.

The consultant _____

_____

7 'Today is a day which will go down in history,' said the factory owner to the workers.

The factory owner _____

_____

8 'The government has consistently failed to support small businesses,' said the reporter.

The reporter _____

_____

Rewriting

For each of the sentences below, write a new sentence as similar as possible in meaning using the word given in CAPITALS. This word must not be altered in any way.

1 The collapse of the company was brought about by a sudden price rise in raw materials.

WALL

_____

2 'If I were you, I wouldn't make any decisions yet,' said Peter to his son.

URGED

_____

3 Products which seem to lack credibility are not popular.

CALL

_____

4 Many people find themselves in difficulties by not paying for goods immediately.

CREDIT

_____

5 Buying old maps was a hobby of John Samson's.

DABBLED

_____

6 'Why don't you invest some of the money you have inherited?' said Susan to William.

SUGGESTED

_____

7 The twins always seem to disagree with each other.

PICKING

_____

8 We have run out of small sizes.

STOCK

_____

Cloze

Cloze development

A The words on the left (1–20) have been taken from the text. Insert them in the correct position in each line. Ignore the sentences which are <u>underlined</u> for the moment.

HOW TO SELL YOURSELF!

1 while	The 28-year-old had spent six years working nights she gained her university
2 to	degree during the day. '<u>I always wanted be a teacher,</u>' she said, '<u>and I worked hard</u>
3 finally	<u>to earn my degree. When I graduated, I was very optimistic.</u>' She had her eye
4 on	a teaching position at a nearby primary school. With the help of friends who teach
5 the	at school, she landed an interview with the Head. '<u>I noticed a tiny ladder in my</u>
6 about	<u>tights earlier,</u>' she recalls, '<u>I thought changing them, but I knew I'd be late if</u>
7 by	<u>I did. And the time I got to the interview, it was enormous. I walked in</u>
8 for	<u>apologizing not looking my best.</u>' The would-be teacher didn't get the job. In fact
9 her	one of her friends told that <u>the Head's only comment was: 'If someone doesn't take</u>
10 an	<u>the time to present her best image at interview, what kind of teacher</u> is she going
11 if	<u>to be?'</u> First impressions are lasting ones. Indeed, you play your cards right,
12 call	you can enjoy the benefits of what sociologists the 'halo effect'. This means that
13 four	if you're viewed positively within the critical first minutes, the person you've met
14 everything	will probably assume you do is positive. Bungle a first encounter, and often the
15 other	interviewer will assume you have a host of negative traits. Worse, he or she may
16 you	not take the time to give a second chance. Most employers believe that those who
17 more	look as if they care about themselves will care about their jobs. So aim
18 across	to come in the best possible light – attractive in the way you dress, in your
19 inside	gestures, facial expressions and in your speech. We know it's what's that counts,
20 as	but research shows that personable people are generally perceived more intelligent,
	likeable and credible.

B Reported speech. Change the direct speech <u>underlined</u> in the article into reported speech. Remember to insert any missing words in the correct place!

animalcrackers

A Does the pronunciation of the letters *dog* change in these words and expressions?

lie dog**go**   in the dog**house**   dog-**eared**

dog**gie paddle**   dog**matic**   lap**dog**

dog**sbody**   dog**ged**

B Match the words and expressions with the meanings 1–8.

1 a small pet
2 with the corners worn
3 in disgrace
4 opinionated

5 a simple swimming stroke
6 constantly troubled
7 someone who has to do the boring work
8 stay motionless

C Now use one of the words or expressions to complete the sentences below.

1 Although he is a good manager, he sometimes comes across as being rather _____.

2 Although it may not be an elegant stroke, many children can do _____.

3 When Sam first joined the staff in the office, he ended up being the _____.

4 Susan is a very strong-willed woman and Simon is a mere _____ to her.

5 His business career was _____ by bad luck.

6 Peter never does anything to help at home so he's always _____.

7 I love this old dictionary, even though it's _____.

8 It's no use _____; I know you're watching TV in there!

Writing

Write a paragraph describing either an advert that appeals to you or one you detest. Say how successful or unsuccessful it is in its objectives.

_____   _____

_____   _____

_____   _____

_____   _____

_____   _____

_____   _____

12 TAKING LIBERTIES

Vocabulary

Crime

Complete this puzzle of words connected with crime to find the name of a famous detective.

1 The student who left the store without paying for the dress was accused of _____.

2 The murderer was _____ to life imprisonment.

3 The boy who tried to burn down the hotel was found guilty of _____.

4 Because he was driving so fast, the police charged my father with _____ driving.

5 The minister committed a massive _____ by using government money for his own purposes.

6 As your jaw and three ribs are broken, the man who attacked you will be charged with _____.

7 The judge asked the _____ to describe exactly what she had seen at the scene of the crime.

8 Many people believe that _____ for offences like burglary are not harsh enough.

9 When he was _____ of the murder, his wife broke down in court.

10 The film star decided to sue the paper for _____ after it printed a story saying he was a drug addict.

11 Millions of people in America watched the _____ of O.J. Simpson on TV.

12 The penalties for tax _____ vary from a fine to many years' imprisonment.

13 At the end of the trial, the jury brought in a unanimous _____ of guilty.

Structure

Use, to use, used to, used to doing, useless

A Complete the following extract from a letter with the correct form of the word *use*, adding any other words that are necessary.

I have been inside for nearly a year now, so I ___am getting used to___ the way things work here. I don't mind getting up early, and I 1 _____ being locked up for a long time every day. Mind you, I never 2 _____ take much exercise anyway, did I?

I am happier too, in a way. When I first arrived, I 3 _____ spend the whole time thinking of how I could escape, what I could 4 _____ to cut through the bars and so on. But I've realized that it 5 _____ trying to get out of here. For one thing, the prison is miles from anywhere, and they would just 6 _____ the dogs to track me down; but the guards also 7 _____ some of the other prisoners as informers, so they know what's going on. So I have accepted my fate and I try to make 8 _____ of the few facilities we have here like the library. It saddens me sometimes when I read something that reminds me of the way things 9 _____ be between us, but I try not to dwell on it, and tell myself that it 10 _____ looking back at the past.

B Write a similar paragraph using the different forms of *use* as above. Begin 'I was once very poor but then I won the lottery...'

They looked shocked and affronted and somehow ashamed. Above all, they looked old. Wexford thought that in the nature of things a woman of seventy ought to be an
05 orphan, ought to have been an orphan for twenty years. This one had been an orphan for scarcely twenty days. Her husband, sitting opposite her, pulling his wispy moustache, slowly and mechanically shaking his head,
10 seemed older than she, perhaps not so many years the junior of his late mother-in-law. He wore a brown cardigan with a small neat darn at one elbow and sheepskin slippers, and when he spoke he snuffled. His wife kept saying she
15 couldn't believe her ears, she couldn't believe it, why were people so wicked? Wexford didn't answer that. He couldn't, though he had often wondered himself.

'My mother died of a stroke,' Mrs Betts said
20 tremulously. 'It was on the death certificate, Dr Moss put it on the death certificate.'

Betts snuffled and wheezed. 'She was ninety-two,' he said in his thick catarrhal voice. 'Ninety-two. I reckon you lot must have got
25 bats in the belfry.'

'I mean,' said Mrs Betts, 'are you saying that Dr Moss was telling untruths? A doctor?'

'Why don't you ask him? We're only ordinary people, the wife and me, we're not educated.
30 Doctor said a cerebral haemorrhage,' Betts stumbled a little over the words, 'and in plain language that's a stroke. That's what he said. Are you saying the wife or me gave mother a stroke? Are you saying that?'

35 'I'm making no allegations, Mr Betts.' Wexford felt uncomfortable, wished himself anywhere but in this newly decorated, paint-smartened house. 'I am merely making enquiries which information received obliges me to do.'

40 'Gossip,' said Mrs Betts bitterly. 'This street's a hotbed of gossip. Pity they've nothing better to do. Oh, I know what they're saying. Half of them turn up their noses and look the other way when I pass them. All except Elsie Parrish, and that
45 goes without saying.'

'She's been a brick,' said her husband. 'A real brick is Elsie.' He stared at Wexford with a kind of timid outrage. 'Haven't you folk got nothing better to do? What about the real crime? What
50 about the muggings and the break-ins?'

Wexford sighed. But he went on doggedly questioning, remembering what the nurse had said, what Dr Moss had said, keeping in the forefront of his mind that motive which was so
55 much more than merely wanting an aged parent out of the way. If he hadn't been a policeman with a profound respect for the law and for human life, he might have felt that these two, or one of them, had been provoked beyond bearing
60 to do murder.

One of them? Or both? Or neither? Ivy Wrangton had either died an unnatural death or else there had been a series of coincidences and unexplained contingencies which were nothing
65 short of incredible.

Old Wives' Tales by Ruth Rendell

A Read this extract from a crime novel.

B Multiple-choice questions. Choose the best answer.

1 Wexford was slightly disconcerted by the fact that
A Mrs Betts had been so old when her mother died.
B Mr Betts was as old as his wife's mother.
C Mrs Betts had lost both of her parents.
D Mr and Mrs Betts both denied his accusations.

2 Mr Betts implies that
A his mother-in-law died of old age.
B the doctor caused his mother-in-law's death.
C the doctor who signed the death certificate made a mistake.
D he cannot fully understand how his mother-in-law died.

3 The inspector is questioning the elderly couple because
A they have been charged with attempted murder.
B he has proof that they are involved with a murder.
C he has a duty to carry out an investigation.
D he does not believe what the doctor said.

4 Mr Betts appears to believe that
A the neighbours have been gossiping about them.
B the police should be concentrating on other offences.
C one particular neighbour has been spreading rumours.
D the people who live near them are snobbish.

5 Wexford feels it is worth questioning the couple about Ivy Wrangton because
A he is certain they both murdered her.
B he knew they were tired of looking after her.
C the circumstances surrounding her death were unusual.
D he was unsure of what their motive may have been.

C Vocabulary. Match the words in **1–8** with **a–h**, their meanings as used in the passage.

1 *affronted* (line 1)   **a** breathed with difficulty

2 *junior* (line 11)   **b** deceased

3 *late* (line 11)   **c** insulted

4 *tremulously* (line 20)   **d** younger than someone

5 *wheezed* (line 22)   **e** with determination

6 *muggings* (line 50)   **f** in a nervous voice

7 *doggedly* (line 51)   **g** concurrences of apparently unrelated events

8 *coincidences* (line 63)

h street attacks

Now use the words above to complete these sentences, making any changes that are necessary.

1 Mr Jackson has inherited the house that belonged to his _____ mother-in-law.

2 He got married late in life to a woman twenty years his _____.

3 Do you think greater police presence on the streets would reduce _____ and vandalism?

4 You'd better give up smoking. You are beginning to _____ terribly.

5 I was grossly _____ when she accused me of stealing from her.

6 The policeman _____ pursued the robbers, and only stopped when they had been brought to justice.

7 Are you really going to New York next week? What a _____! So am I.

8 The unhappy child asked _____ if she could go home to her mother.

Rewriting: Gerunds and infinitives

For each of the sentences below, write a new sentence as similar as possible in meaning using the word given in CAPITALS. **This word must not be altered in any way.**

1 When he returned home, he found that his flat had been ransacked.

FIND

_____

2 If you want to catch the 5.15 train you will have to leave early.

MEAN

_____

3 I really wish I hadn't said what I did.

REGRET

_____

4 It's a waste of time to try to make me change my mind.

POINT

_____

5 The bank manager said he wouldn't lend me what I needed.

UNWILLING

_____

6 The Prime Minister is not going to resign.

INTENTION

_____

7 Mozart's last work was unfinished when he died.

WITHOUT

_____

8 Jack got promoted before almost anyone else.

BE

_____

9 Emma was very surprised when she heard she had passed the exam.

CAME

_____

10 I'll always remember the first time I saw the Pyramids.

SEEING

_____

Cloze

Read this article about detective stories. Fill each of the numbered blanks with <u>one</u> suitable word.

Detective fiction __1__ to the same psychological need in us which up __2__ the beginning of the century was __3__ by religious accounts of what __4__ to be called the Problem of Evil. For that, __5__ essence, is what every detective story is – a problem of evil.

Detective stories __6__ to work the same theme over and __7__ again; they are our secular __8__ of the story of the Garden of Eden in __9__ they depict a relatively calm scene shattered by the intrusion of 'foul unnatural murder'. However, they __10__ a distinctively modern element by exploring the hope that some force for good, in other __11__ the detective, can work __12__ the identity and unnatural motives of the hidden villain, and so point the __13__ to paradise regained. This is a particularly prominent __14__ of Agatha Christie stories, __15__ the innocent couples all pair off nicely at the __16__.

Moreover, we know from dreams that the human mind still explores its worries __17__ of all in dramatised story-form, __18__ to and underneath all its intellectual thinking. __19__ seems certain therefore that people will continue to enjoy reading detective stories, because they __20__ with questions of good and evil in an accessible way.

Vocabulary review

Choose the word which best completes each sentence.

1 You can have my moped if you like; now that I've got a car, it's no ___ to me.
 A worth B use C value D point

2 A good doctor should not get too emotionally involved with patients, but should also not become completely ___ to their suffering.
 A uninterested B indifferent C nonchalant D apathetic

3 The judge said that the murderer had shown a callous ___ for human life.
 A disregard B ignorance C inattention D omission

4 The jury decided that the seven-year-old boy could not be held ___ for his actions.
 A responsible B guilty C culpable D answerable

5 The suspect's version of events was not ___ with the accounts of the other witnesses.
 A confirmed B related C consistent D corroborated

6 I don't know how you can find anything in your office. The place is a(n) ___ shambles.
 A full B entire C whole D complete

7 However aggrieved you may feel, it would be wrong to try and ___ the law into your own hands.
 A bring B hold C take D seize

8 He felt ___ that at long last he was safe, and fell into a deep sleep.
 A resigned B shocked C appalled D relieved

9 After the accident, the two drivers' ___ of exactly what happened were very different.
 A narrations B versions C evidence D renditions

10 If you were lucky ___ to have a house abroad, how often would you go there?
 A so B enough C as D for

Vocabulary

animalcrackers

A Find synonyms or paraphrases to show the difference between these words.

apprehend comprehend reprehend

Are the letters *hen* pronounced differently in the word '*phen*omenon'?

B Now use the four words in sentences of your own.

Writing

Adding details

One of the features that can make a story sound more authentic and interesting is the addition of minor extra details. Look at the following example.

VERSION 1

I have only once in my life had an experience that was frightening. I was living in a farmhouse which I had rented. One night, I was woken up by the sound of someone at the window. It was past midnight. I walked to the top of the stairs.

Comment:

There are no grammatical mistakes in the first version, but the writer has missed a lot of opportunities to make the story more interesting. For example, we do not know where the house was, what time of year it was, what the writer was doing there, and so on. We are given little impression of what the inside of the house was like, where the sound was coming from, or how the writer reacted. Compare the second version, which contains the same words but with some additional details.

VERSION 2

I have only once in my life had an experience that was frightening. I was living on the Yorkshire moors in a remote farmhouse which I had rented for the winter so that I could complete my thesis. One night in early February, I was woken up by the sound of someone rattling and tapping at the window in the sitting room downstairs. I looked over at the eerie glow of the alarm clock on the bedside table; it was thirteen minutes past midnight. For a moment, I was unsure of what I should do, but then I put on my dressing gown, opened the bedroom door and walked slowly down the darkened corridor to the top of the stairs.

Complete the story, by adding extra details to the following paragraph. Before you write, look at the notes below.

I went downstairs. I opened the door but I couldn't see anything. I went across to the window. Suddenly I saw the face of a man. He looked at me then ran away. I ran outside but there was no trace of him.

Notes:

1 Think of an explanation for the face at the window – this could be a ghost story, or the man could be some kind of criminal or someone known to the writer.

2 Consider questions **a**–**k** when you are planning the extra details.

a How did the writer walk down the stairs and open the door?

b What could the writer hear in the darkness?

c Did the writer peer through the door or fling it open and switch on the light?

d How was the writer feeling when crossing the room?

e What did the face of the man look like – age, height, his eyes, his clothes?

f Was the man known to the writer at all?

g How did the man and the writer react when they saw each other?

h How did the man run? Quickly? With a limp? In which direction?

i How quickly did the writer give chase?

j What did the writer do after seeing the man had disappeared?

k What happened in the end?

Reading and Summary

A Read this article about a circus with a difference.

sweat, sawdust & surrealism

Jon Wilde, *himself the offspring of tightrope walkers, reports on the new wave of circus performers.*

There was a time in the not-too-distant past when everyone, it seemed, loved a circus. Up and down the land, children would
05 anticipate the annual visit of the big top to their locality with feverish excitement. Entire families would troop along and thrill to the sight of elephants jumping through hoops
10 and scantily-clad ladies being fired from cannons. Long after the last tent pegs had been pulled up from the village greens, children would gather to fantasize about a make-
15 believe world of becoming trapeze artists and running off to join the greatest show on earth.

However, the circus has suffered a dramatic fall from grace in the last
20 twenty years. There are many reasons for this sudden decline: not only have there been spiralling costs, but punitive levels of taxes on entertainment have also played their
25 part. Without doubt, though, the biggest reason for the circus's decline has been increasing public indifference. Animal rights protests against the use of animals for
30 entertainment, along with tabloid headlines exposing ill-treatment of circus animals, created a climate that was at first unsympathetic and then openly hostile. At the same time, the
35 circus found itself competing with videos and computer games for the attentions of youngsters.

As the traditional circus found itself in the deep waters of
40 unfashionability, attempts were made to adapt to changing public tastes.

Even so, despite the efforts of novelty circuses, like *Gary Glitter's Rock 'n' Roll Big Top*, to appeal to the
45 mainstream, the traditional family audience remained largely indifferent. However, this situation is set to change dramatically with the launch of Phillip Gandey's *Cirque Surreal*.
50 Not only does this innovative 'designer circus' feature a host of international artists but it also promises to lure the stay-at-home families back to the ring with a
55 breath-taking non-animal show that has been specially choreographed to music by Rick Wakeman, one of rock music's premier showmen.

The name of Gandey has been
60 synonymous with quality circuses for three generations now. Indeed, it was Phillip's grandfather who started Gandey's Circus at the turn of the century. Philip himself made his
65 début in the ring singing at the tender age of two. By the age of six, he had progressed to playing the clown, throwing knives, riding the trapeze, playing drums and juggling
70 bottles. By this time, he had decided that the sweat-and-sawdust life was definitely for him. As Gandey's made a name for itself dwarfing all other travelling circuses in Britain, Phillip
75 spent his youth moving from town to town, receiving his education in more than 400 schools.

'There's an old saying about the circus,' he says, 'that once you get a
80 bit of sawdust in your eyes, you can never get it out. That's certainly true for me. The spell was cast before I

was out of nappies. I've seen all the changes through the years, but I've
85 never lost my enthusiasm for it.'

When Phillip was seventeen, his father died and Phillip inherited the family business. He needed little persuasion to take over but he
90 realized that he would have to go down a different route to lure back audiences. Having introduced the *Chinese State Circus* to Britain, he began to develop the idea of the
95 *Cirque Surreal*. 'If you look at the dictionary definition of 'surreal',' he says, 'it refers to a dream-like state, or something that is over and above human experience. That's the kind of
100 show that I wanted to create. Something that was astonishing to watch without being shocking.'

Having recruited top international acts from Cuba, France and Russia,
105 the show began to fall into place. The music of Rick Wakeman proved to be the final piece of the jigsaw. 'The important part of the *Cirque Surreal*,' says Gandey, 'is that every element
110 has to be of the highest quality. That included the music. As well as being an exceptional musician, Rick is an extremely charismatic performer. It's the sheer quality of Rick's
115 performance that gives the show that extra bit of class. But there'll also be high-wire acts, flying trapeze and ballet performed in the air. There are some incredible speciality acts,
120 including the most amazing jugglers and contortionists you'll ever see. The whole thing is literally an out-of-this-world spectacular!'

Jon Wilde, Livewire Magazine

B Multiple-choice questions. Choose the best answer.

1 Not so long ago, after the circus had finished its annual performances, local children would
A help the circus folk to take down the big top.
B gather to wave the circus folk goodbye.
C dream of becoming performers themselves.
D create their own circuses on village greens.

2 In more recent years, the decline of the circus can be largely attributed to
A the prohibitive prices of tickets.
B the rise of the high-tech cinema.
C unsuccessful advertising campaigns.
D the disapproval of potential audiences.

3 What confirmed Phillip Gandey's choice of the circus as a career?
A He was asked to appear in Gary Glitter's novelty circus.
B His parents took him to a circus when he was only two.
C He discovered that a visiting circus needed young performers.
D He realized at an early age that the circus was in his blood.

4 When he was 17, Phillip decided to
A take over a well-known rival circus.
B travel the world looking for original acts.
C follow religiously in his father's footsteps.
D create a marketable circus troupe.

5 According to Phillip Gandey, what kind of performer is Rick Wakeman?
A inspiring
B spontaneous
C enthusiastic
D classical

6 What is the underlying motivation behind the 'new wave of circus'?
A to avoid any adverse publicity from those opposed to circuses
B to offer a classical rather than traditional form of entertainment
C to provide entertainment which will take the audience's breath away
D to re-establish the traditional circus as a form of popular entertainment

C Comprehension. Explain the meaning of the following as they are used in the article.

1 *scantily-clad* (line 10)
2 *a dramatic fall from grace* (line 19)
3 *found itself in the waters of unfashionability* (line 38)
4 *appeal to the mainstream* (line 44)
5 *dwarfing all other travelling circuses* (line 73)
6 *to lure back audiences* (line 91)
7 *the final piece of the jigsaw* (line 107)
8 *jugglers and contortionists* (line 120)

D Summary. In 60–80 words, summarize the reasons for the decline of the traditional circus and the methods employed by Phillip Gandey to try and ensure the survival of circuses.

Vocabulary review

A Choose the word which best completes each sentence.

1 The violinist was ___ by the reception he received from the audience.
A overburdened B overreached C overwhelmed
D overpowered

2 Children's video games also played their part in ___ the fate of the circus.
A securing B concluding C sealing D settling

3 An article ___ the ill-treatment of some circus animals appeared in the national press.
A imposing B composing C reposing D exposing

4 The word 'severe' is a(n) ___ of 'punitive'.
A antonym B homonym C synonym D homophone

5 'Designer circuses' – ___ example is the *Cirque Surreal* – look set to redress the circus's fall from grace.
A for B like C such as D one such

6 The soprano's performance last night was ___ shattering – a window broke!
A literally B laterally C latterly D locally

7 Pavarotti made his ___ on stage many years ago at an international competition in Wales.
A initiation B début C inauguration D induction

8 The audience was ___ to what the young choreographer was trying to do.
A unenthusiastic B disrespectful C unsympathetic
D disinterested

B Complete the table of words taken from this unit.

Noun	Verb	Adjective
		original
	created	
		persuasive
	compete	
unfashionability	—	
		indifferent
publicity		
	progressed	
		prohibitive
		enthusiastic

Rewriting

For each of the sentences below, write a new sentence as similar as possible in meaning using the word given in CAPITALS. **This word must not be altered in any way.**

1 Under the circumstances the company can do little but accept the situation.

   MAKE

   _____

2 No suitable play was found by the company to draw audiences back to the theatre.

   FAILED

   _____

3 The least little problem and the director always panics!

   MOLEHILL

   _____

4 I suddenly realized why the audience was being so hostile.

   DAWNED

   _____

5 There was a loud scream from backstage immediately after the concert ended.

   SOONER

   _____

6 The actors did not realize that the scenery was about to fall on them.

   LITTLE

   _____

7 The 1970s saw the rise to fame of rock musician Rick Wakeman.

   NAME

   _____

8 The performer learned how to juggle by practising day after day.

   ONLY

   _____

9 A good example of an out-of-this-world experience is the *Cirque Surreal.*

   EXEMPLIFIES

   _____

10 Entertainment must be sympathetic to the needs of its audience if it is to be popular.

   WITHOUT

   _____

Blank-filling

Fill each of the blanks in the following sentences with a suitable word or phrase.

1 Not only _____, but they were short of time as well.

2 Not a word _____ when she told him the news.

3 The circus's only hope of _____ is to adapt to modern ways of thinking.

4 Gandey would like _____ of as the saviour of the circus.

5 Many people know next _____ about contortionists but they would be interested in going to see them perform.

6 To the north of the village lay the river, while _____ the rolling hills.

7 Not until _____ did we realize that we had forgotten the tickets.

8 Juggling is difficult but if you persevere you will soon _____ of it.

9 It is with regret that we have to _____ your kind invitation to dinner on the 22nd.

10 Word _____ wildfire that the circus was coming to town.

Positive or Negative?

The words below are taken from the text on page 66. Sort them into two groups depending on whether they are used positively or negatively.

1 feverish excitement   7 innovative

2 indifference   8 to fantasize

3 spiralling costs   9 to thrill to

4 punitive taxes   10 a dramatic fall from grace

5 breath-taking   11 the greatest show on earth

6 a sudden decline   12 unsympathetic

+	−

Cloze

Read this continuation of the article on page 66 and fill each of the numbered blanks with <u>one</u> suitable word.

Wakeman rose to the dizzy heights of __1__ in the early 1970s as a keyboardist, but he has __2__ pursued a multi-faceted career. Not only has he produced mega-selling albums like *Journey to the Centre of the Earth*, but he has also collaborated with international artists, appearing in productions whose casts have __3__ artists such as Chaka Khan, Tim Rice and other household __4__. Since __5__ out of fashion at the height of the punk movement, he has __6__ and won much-publicized battles with bankruptcy and, in more __7__ years, has largely concentrated his energies on film soundtracks and New Age music. Wakeman has always exhibited a fondness for spectacular events, and __8__ his current work with the *Cirque Surreal* as a natural extension of previous productions like his celebrated mid-Seventies version of *The Myths and Legends of King Arthur*, __9__ was staged on ice, complete with full orchestra and choir. 'I'm __10__ to things that have a touch of the spectacular about them,' he says. 'As a boy, I __11__ look forward all year to the circus. Like most kids at the time, I regarded the circus in the summer as __12__ of growing up. Even though circuses went into __13__ I have to say that I never really __14__ my fascination with them. __15__ I leapt at the chance of working with the *Cirque Surreal*. Musically __16__, it's an enormous challenge. But, at the __17__ of the day, it's the visuals that are going to grab the attention. It's such an incredible visual feast that I __18__ it almost impossible to describe. There's no __19__ to capture in words the effect it has on an audience. Really, you'll have to see it with your __20__ eyes.'

Writing

Write a formal reply to the invitation below saying that you are either able or unable to attend.

Phillip Gandey
requests the pleasure of your company at

A GALA OPENING OF

CIRQUE SURREAL

at
The Fortune Theatre,
Main Street West
on Saturday 9 October
at 7.30

—— R.S.V.P. ——
The Fortune Theatre

Write a short paragraph outlining your attitude towards circuses.

_____   _____

_____   _____

_____   _____

_____   _____

_____   _____

_____   _____

_____   _____

_____   _____

Vocabulary

animalcrackers

A Combine the word _fly_ with the beginnings and endings below.

leaf

sheet   away

tip

fly   paper

brief   horse

er   over

chief

Which two words are pronounced differently from the others?

B Match the words you have made with the meanings below.

1 mainly
2 canvas cover over a tent
3 blank page at the beginning or end of a book
4 dump illegally
5 sticky paper used to trap flies
6 bridge carrying one road over another
7 difficult to control, e.g. of hair
8 concisely
9 small handbill or leaflet
10 large fly; the females suck mammals' blood

THE WORLD IN OUR HANDS

Cloze

Read this passage about astronomy. Fill each of the numbered blanks with <u>one</u> suitable word.

Astronomy is one of the oldest of all the sciences, and one on which ancient civilizations 1 _____ considerably. The Mayans and Egyptians, for example, 2 _____ hold religious ceremonies according to the stars. Later, 3 _____ their civilization was at 4 _____ height, the Ancient Greeks developed a sophisticated model of the universe which 5 _____ them to navigate by the stars.

Most ancient civilizations assumed the earth to 6 _____ the centre of the universe and it was 7 _____ until 1610, after the first telescope had been invented, 8 _____ Galileo was able to prove that, 9 _____ to popular belief, the earth in 10 _____ revolved round the sun.

Telescopes have improved greatly since then but the exponential 11 _____ of cities in the 20th century has brought new difficulties in 12 _____ the glow from them interferes with the very dim signals from the stars. A partial 13 _____ has been to build observatories where this interference can be cut down to a 14 _____, and the largest observatory in the world, Mauna Kea, is set in the crater of a dormant 15 _____ in Hawaii.

However, astronomers realized that 16 _____ the science was to progress, radically 17 _____ measures would have to be taken, and this 18 _____ to the building of the Hubble Space Telescope, which was launched in 1990. As Hubble operates in space, it is completely 19 _____ by either light or atmospheric pollution. It can detect galaxies that have never been seen, and can transmit images of the most distant stars at the very 20 _____ of the universe.

Vocabulary review

Expressions

Choose the word which best completes each sentence.

1 I was so tired that when I got into bed I went out like a _____.
A flame B candle C spark D light

2 The prisoner's case was re-opened after some new evidence _____ to light.
A rose B brought C came D appeared

3 I wouldn't take a chemistry book on holiday as a little light _____ .
A information B reading C reference D literature

4 I was upset that my two best friends _____ me in the dark about going away on holiday together.
A held B kept C put D set

5 After months of depression, I am beginning to see the light at the end of the _____.
A road B passage C tunnel D line

6 My brother tried to _____ light of my obvious disapproval of his behaviour, but I said I was very serious.
A bring B talk C make D think

A Read this extract from a travel book, together with the account below it.

The ascent of the Pyramid though fatiguing is perfectly safe. The traveller selects two or three helpers. With one holding each hand, and the third pushing behind, he begins the ascent of
05 *the steps. The ascent can be made in 10–15 minutes, but in hot weather especially, the traveller is recommended to take nearly double the time.*

From *Egypt and the Sudan*, Karl Baedeker, 8th edition.

10 Later that afternoon I climbed the Great Pyramid from the north-west corner, taking Baedeker's suggested ten minutes without any helper to push, pull and support me. The easiest way is from the north-east corner, but as it is now forbidden to
15 climb it from any corner I wanted to be out of sight of the Pyramids police station, which is situated on the edge of the plateau below the east face. The top, truncated by the removal of the limestone, is about twelve yards square, and I was
20 the only one on it.

The view could scarcely have been more extensive. Across the river, below the cliffs of the Mokattam Hills, from where much of the 6,000,000 tons of stone used to build this single
25 pyramid were quarried, were the mosques and spectacular minarets of Muslim Cairo, the largest city in Africa, and the great labyrinthine cemeteries. Down towards the Nile, to the north of Old Cairo, was the modern city with the high
30 buildings rising above it, not enough of them, as in Manhattan, to form groves of forests which give

them an air of majesty, but in melancholy twos or threes, or completely isolated.

I was now joined by a host of 'Nagamas',
35 members of an itinerant tribe, who had seen me climb the pyramid, and now, with their insatiable demands for money and their constant tugging at my clothing, very nearly succeeded in making me lose my temper.

40 Before retreating I took one more look over the edge. It was Friday, the Muslim day of rest, and the lower courses of the Great Pyramid, and to a lesser extent that of King Chephren were filled, although the sun was setting now, with happy
45 bands of modern Egyptians, couples and families and groups of students, most of whom had come out from Cairo or Giza by car, shared taxi or on motorcycles, to spend the day picknicking, singing – sometimes to the accompaniment of
50 musical instruments – or listening to radios, while others played football on the level expanses at the foot of the Great Pyramid. Almost everyone, if I had passed close enough to them that morning, had asked me if I liked the country, if I liked them,
55 and if they were eating or drinking, had invited me to join them. The proximity of these Egyptians also ensured in some mysterious way freedom from the attention of the Nagamas. What a difference, I thought, it made in one's relations to
60 them, to be no longer a member of an occupying army, as I once had been.

When I reached the bottom I was met by the same tourist policeman who had admitted me to the Pyramid that morning.
65 'No climbing of the Great Pyramid,' he said severely. It was as if we had never met before. 'Fine is fifteen Egyptian pounds.'

'I haven't got fifteen Egyptian pounds,' I said. It was true.
70 'OK,' he said. 'You give me one Egyptian pound.'

'OK,' I said. I liked this policeman. He reduced justice to a level of simplicity.

'OK,' he said, pocketing the money, saluting smartly and moving off, having successfully
75 solved yet another problem for a foreign tourist in distress.

On The Shores of the Mediterranean by Eric Newby

B Multiple-choice questions. Choose the best answer.

1 The writer implies that the advice from the travel book he quotes is
   A very clear.
   B inaccurate.
   C complicated.
   D rather absurd.

2 The writer chose to climb the north-west face of the Great Pyramid because
A he was unable to get any help.
B he did not want the police to see him.
C it was the most direct route.
D the easiest route was forbidden.

3 From the top of the Pyramid he could see
A workers in the quarry.
B the trees of modern Cairo.
C ancient burial places.
D large numbers of skyscrapers.

4 The Nagamas had followed him to the top of the Pyramid to
A ask him for money.
B find out what he was doing.
C get a closer look at him.
D warn him about the police.

5 What does the writer feel about the local visitors to the Pyramids?
A They were irritatingly noisy.
B They were behaving in an inappropriate manner.
C They were very hospitable and polite.
D They were very annoying.

C Vocabulary. Match the words **1–6** with their meanings **a–f** as used in the passage.

1 *truncated* (line 18)	**a**	made shorter
2 *labyrinthine* (line 27)	**b**	full of complicated passages and tunnels
3 *host* (line 34)		
4 *insatiable* (line 36)	**c**	allowed in
5 *admitted* (line 63)	**d**	difficulty
6 *distress* (line 76)	**e**	unable to be satisfied
	f	crowd

Now complete these sentences with the words above.

1 The lifeboat went to sea to rescue a boat in _____.

2 There are still some old-fashioned clubs where women are not _____.

3 It is easy to get lost in the _____ corridors and passages of the palace.

4 The newspapers printed a very _____ version of the Minister's speech.

5 There are a whole _____ of reasons why I want to move away from here.

6 The media's appetite for stories about the Royal Family is _____.

D Summary. In 60–80 words, summarize the encounters the writer had with the local people that day.

Forms of the future

Read through the following dialogue. Then select the correct forms of the future.

James: Hello. The English Centre.

Rachel: Hello, James – this is Rachel here. Listen, |1 *will / shall*| you do me a favour?

James: Yes, of course.

Rachel: Well, I |2 *am giving / give*| Class 3 a mock exam this morning, so could you look after them for fifteen minutes or so?

James: Fine, but what's the matter?

Rachel: Oh, the wretched car |3 *won't start / isn't going to start,*| so I |4 *catch / am going to catch*| the 8.15 train from Westbury.

James: |5 *Shall / Will*| I start them off, then?

Rachel: No, it's all right. Just tell them I |6 *am going to be / am being*| a bit late but I |7 *will be / will have been*| there – and do make it absolutely clear to them that they |8 *are not to / will not*| look at the question papers until I get there. I'm afraid they're sitting on my desk! You know what Class 3 are like – if you give them half a chance, they |9 *will have looked up / will have been looking up*| all the answers by the time I get there.

James: OK, that's no problem, I |10 *'ll / 'm going to*| tell them. By the way, I thought you |11 *would get / were getting*| a new car?

Rachel: Yes, I |12 *was going to / would,*| but my father says that he |13 *is to get rid of / will be getting rid of*| his soon, so I thought I'd wait. Listen, there's someone at the door – I expect it |14 *will be / will have been*| the man from the garage. See you later! And thanks, James.

Vocabulary review

The environment

Choose the word which best completes each sentence.

1 Ecologists are concerned about the dumping of ___ waste at sea.
A poisonous B noxious C toxic D venomous

2 The increase in CFCs is thought to have damaged the ozone ___.
A course B layer C strata D level

3 The pollution from car exhausts could be reduced by the use of catalytic ___ .
A transformers B exchangers C alternators
D converters

4 The countries of the West are noted for their conspicuous ___ of energy.
A absorption B consumption C dissipation
D depletion

5 If the theories of ___ warming are correct, sea levels will soon begin to rise.
A global B terrestrial C international D universal

6 The numbers of tigers worldwide are falling, and they are therefore an ___ species.
A endangered B extinct C imperilled D exposed

7 Many ancient monuments are being ___ away by acid rain.
A eroded B rubbed C eaten D faded

8 It is likely that ___ will lead to severe food shortages in the next century.
A overmanning B overcrowding C overpopulation
D overgrowth

Vocabulary

animalcrackers

A Match the words on the left with the meanings a–e on the right.

1 remuneration   a stupefaction

2 emulation   b reward/pay

3 emulsion   c a food additive

4 emulsifier   d a type of paint

5 bemusement   e rivalry through imitation

In which two pairs of words are the letters *emu* pronounced in the same way?

B Hidden emus. Each of these words, which contain an *emu*, has three meanings, given on the right. Match the meanings to the words, using them to fill the blanks.

1 m e _ _ u _ _   a a kind of shoe

              b a radio wavelength

2 m e _ _ u _   c a Roman god

              d what a stubborn person is compared to

3 m u _ e   e the middle degree of something

              f a person with psychic powers

              g the offspring of a horse and an ass

              h a planet

              i a metal

B Match the following words with their meanings as used in the article.

1	*symbiosis* (line 22)	**a** bait (to divert attention)
2	*continuum* (line 25)	**b** revelation
3	*construct* (line 33)	**c** something which goes on for ever
4	*hoax* (line 37)	**d** mutually beneficial relationship
5	*disclosure* (line 45)	**e** fabrication
6	*decoy* (line 67)	**f** humorous or malicious deception

C Explain the meaning of the following words and phrases from the text.

1 *a storm in a teacup* (line 11)
2 *every nook and cranny* (line 60)
3 *not to mince words* (line 99)
4 *we've been taken for a ride* (line 101)
5 *suckers* (line 116)
6 *Are we being kept in the dark?* (line 119)
7 *a leap of the imagination* (line 129)

D Multiple-choice questions. Choose the best answer.

1 According to the first newspaper theory, what kind of relationship do Liam and Patsy have with the media?
A uneasy
B mutually advantageous
C light-hearted
D disastrous

2 According to the second theory, what was the real reason behind the band's expensive charade?
A to show their fans they do things in style
B to snatch the limelight from their competitors
C to prevent media presence at the wedding
D to drum up publicity for their new album

3 Why is the third theory unlikely?
A It was put forward by Oasis fans themselves.
B It has not been confirmed by Liam and Patsy.
C It was suggested by a tabloid newspaper.
D It has a ring of media manipulation about it.

4 According to the fourth theory, what has really happened?
A Patsy and Liam have called their wedding off.
B The wedding has been postponed due to work commitments.
C The media has made a laughing stock out of the public.
D The band no longer has the confidence of the media.

E Summary. In 60–80 words, summarize the five different theories put forward by the newspaper.

> **NOTE:**
> *It may interest you to know that Liam and Patsy did actually marry a short time later.*

Grammatical errors

A Read this newspaper article quickly to find out what day it was written on.

Brian moves like the clappers...
to save national celebration

THIS morning Brian Tipper was trying making light of a rumour that he had saved the New Year for revellers country-wide. Nor it was an idle rumour, for, as Big Ben struck midnight, Brian Tipper breathed a timely sigh of relief. It was thanks to him that the rest of the country was able to welcome in the New Year with the traditional countdown of the bell's famous chimes. Mr Tipper has spent the evening in freezing temperatures at the top of the clock tower made sure the fragile workings were in perfect order. Plummeting temperatures and an icy east wind had froze the delicate mechanism just hours beforehand and Mr Tipper was on standby for just such an emergency. The problem first noticed at 6 p.m. when a retired engineer called the Palace of Westminster to say that the bell, that is hit by hammers, sounded dull. Mr Tipper was spending hours lengthening and weighing the hammers that they hit the bell at the right pitch. 'I wish it hasn't been such a cold night, though,' said Mr Tipper later. 'I'm not using to working in such temperatures. But I couldn't let the country down now, could I? I'm absolutely pleased to have been able to fix everything.' The Arctic wind showed no signs to loosen its icy grip yesterday. With the wind-chill factor, the mercury dropped to a record-break minus 21°C in parts of the south-east.

B Now read it again more slowly. Underline the 14 grammatical errors and correct them.

Cloze

Read this newspaper story and fill each of the numbered blanks with <u>one</u> suitable word.

PARACHUTISTS SURVIVE

Two sky-divers taking part **1** _____ the Australian National Skydiving Championships at Corowa, 335 miles south-west of Sydney, survived a 1,600ft fall **2** _____ colliding in mid-air. Hundreds of spectators, **3** _____ were watching the display at the time, looked **4** _____ in horror as the parachutes became tangled and the men plunged **5** _____ earth. The two men landed in a paddock and, **6** _____ injured, both survived to tell the tale. Geoff Divco was taken to hospital **7** _____ a fractured skull, but his jumping partner, Jerome Rich, was suffering **8** _____ only minor bruising. Safety officer Gary Myors said, 'Basically, they just ran **9** _____ each other. The accident was brought **10** _____ by the collision of the two parachutes after they had opened. Ropes wrapped around the two men as they fell, **11** _____ them from releasing their back-up chutes to break their fall.' 'We certainly didn't expect to be as lucky **12** _____ we were,' they said last night.

Vocabulary

Expressions

Use one of the words suggested by the drawings to complete each of the expressions in the sentences below.

1 You realize that, if production doesn't improve, the Managing Director will throw the _____ at us.

2 Pam's new boy-friend is no fun at all. In fact, he's a real wet _____.

3 Michael and Rachel were engaged for five years before they finally tied the _____ .

4 After what was a very poor start, the children have turned over a new _____ and are getting down to work with some enthusiasm.

5 I can't stand _____ critics – they're always so negative when they express their opinions about something.

6 We don't know how the press got _____ of the forthcoming wedding, but they turned up in force to cover it.

Making sense of headlines. Can you explain what these news stories are probably about?

HEAD GETS FOOT IN DOOR

Police found safe under blanket

Skeleton staff in hospital

Passengers hit by cancelled trains

Blank-filling

Fill each of the blanks in the following sentences with a suitable word or phrase.

1 After several unsuccessful attempts to solve the problem, the engineer finally _____ with a solution.

2 In addition _____ articles for newspapers, the journalist is also a novelist.

3 The new computer can't have broken down, we _____ installed last week.

4 It _____ come as a terrible shock when you found out that you had been betrayed like that.

5 Although Sam _____ experience, he managed to get a job with the newspaper.

6 Please don't _____ amiss when I say that some improvements need to be made to this report you have written.

7 No _____ hard the manager tries, he never seems to win the support of his staff.

8 If you _____ lines, you'll realize that the company has kept us in the dark about its future plans.

9 The current financial crisis means that services will be cut and many public buildings will _____ with closure.

10 The newspaper likes _____ of as a 'quality' paper.

Transformations

Finish each sentence in such a way that it means exactly the same as the one before it.

1 Mr Tipper's wife was very sorry she couldn't celebrate the New Year with her husband.

Mrs Tipper greatly_____

2 The tabloids provide news and entertainment.

Not only _____

3 The journalists only heard about the changes to the wedding plans when they arrived at the venue.

It was only _____

4 The minister's involvement in that corruption scandal has tarnished his reputation.

The minister is under a _____

5 I wasn't as patient with the children as I could have been.

I wish_____

6 They think that the band has split up many times before.

The band_____

7 The students didn't pay enough attention during the training session so they aren't able to follow their instructions correctly.

If the trainees_____

8 The weather was dreadful so the basketball match was cancelled.

If it hadn't_____

9 The supermarket closed before David arrived in the car park.

By the time _____

10 Success in the academic field depends on your ability to amass qualifications.

The more_____

11 'I'm going to drive you home, Jim,' said Susan.

Susan insisted_____

12 We finished dinner and, a few moments later, Mrs Jones arrived on the doorstep.

Hardly_____

Rewriting

For each of the sentences below, write a new sentence as similar as possible in meaning using the word given in CAPITALS. This word must not be altered in any way.

1 Technical skills are needed to operate this new machinery.

DEMANDS

_____

2 We had to wait ages for the plane to take off, so we decided to have a meal in the restaurant.

KILL

_____

3 There's nothing new about crimes of passion.

HILLS

_____

4 I saw a television programme last month which was very similar to this one.

BEARS

_____

5 Just as the burglar was breaking the jeweller's window, the police arrived.

RED-HANDED

_____

6 Susan was intending to go to university but she's apparently changed her mind.

SEEMS

_____

7 We disapprove of tabloid sensationalism in this office.

FROWNED

_____

8 Marriage did not seem to be what Patsy and Liam wanted.

SECOND

_____

9 Claire suddenly realized what a blunder she had made.

DAWNED

_____

10 You must accept the fact that this part of your life has come to an end.

RESIGN

_____

Vocabulary animal**crackers**

Use the names of these animals to complete the sentences below. You need to use some more than once.

1 The governing party will always try to find a scape _____ if anything goes radically wrong.

2 What on earth have you been doing? You look like a drowned _____ !

3 That birthday present's not too bad. Anyway, you shouldn't look a gift _____ in the mouth!

4 I wish the management would make a decision and stop playing _____ and _____ with us!

5 When Sam first started teaching at the primary school he hated it. He felt like a _____ out of water.

6 It's sad to lose touch with a friend but there are plenty more _____ in the sea.

7 Sarah turned out to be a real _____ in the grass when she betrayed us.

8 Mark went skiing for the first time last month and he took to it like a _____ to water!

9 We are discussing _making_ money not _spending_ it. That's an entirely different kettle of _____

10 Molly has resigned. She's fed up with doing all the _____ work around the office!

ANSWER KEY

Reading
A 1T 2F 3F 4T 5T 6F 7T

B 1 *But do you really want to know?*
Will my life change as a result of my glance into this crystal ball?
Will I turn into a wet blanket, or become a real drag?
2 *Look on the bright side!*
3 *a real drag*
chap
4 *You may want to know*
You might prefer to select one

Other devices the writer uses to involve the reader more actively in her experience:
Use of the present tense to tell the story,
e.g. *He says; He congratulates me*
Use of quoted speech:
"You have one copy of"

C 1 (dis) B 2 (app) A 3 (app) C 4 (dis) B
5 (dis) B 6 (dis) A 7 (dis) B 8 (app) B

D 1c 2a 3b

Vocabulary Expressions with *come*
1 round 2 down with 3 out with
4 to the point 5 to terms with
6 down heavily on 7 in for/up against
8 up with

Structure Rewriting
1 The children would rather cycle than walk.
2 Eating / If you eat less fatty food (it) will save you (from) having to try to lose weight.
3 When I saw the condition of the patient, it brought (it) home to me how serious his illness was. / Seeing the condition of the patient brought (it) home to me how serious his illness was.
4 Accidents can be prevented by taking care when we cross the road.
5 Eating sensibly not only improves our health but also increases our longevity. / Not only does eating sensibly improve our health, but it also increases our longevity.
6 It's high time you went and saw / went to see a doctor about those spots!
7 Having (several) interests in common brought Sue and Bob together initially.
8 The accident victim managed to pull through although his condition was serious. / Although the accident victim's condition was serious, he managed to pull through.
9 Dr Peters is widely regarded as being the best surgeon in his field.
10 The Annual General Meeting was put off due to / because of an argument between the management and the staff.

Vocabulary Parts of the body
1 forehead 2 eyebrow 3 palm
4 cheek(bone) 5 shoulder 6 wrist
7 elbow 8 thigh 9 knuckle 10 knee
11 shin 12 ankle

Cloze and Summary
A 1 played
2 regarded / seen / viewed / considered
3 the 4 idea / thought / prospect
5 if / should 6 not / never 7 well
8 where 9 demands / requires / takes
10 any 11 for 12 who 13 that / which
14 pleasing 15 on 16 which
17 greater / keener 18 part 19 in
20 to

B *Points to include:*
1 Appalled because of the numbers of animals needing treatment in such a place.
2 Optimistic because of
a the hospital staff's excellent reputation for taking care of the animals.
b the staff's commitment to finding the animals a suitable home afterwards.
c the luxurious surroundings in which the animals find themselves.

Structure
Defining and non-defining clauses
1 d The shaggiest dogs, which are a mixture of breeds, rub shoulders with the more exotic breeds.
2 c In 1995, 2,044 dogs had to be put to sleep, which gave us no cause to celebrate.
3 a Colonel Green, who has worked at the home for three and a half years, has witnessed the ravages of war all over the world. / Colonel Green, who has witnessed the ravages of war all over the world, has worked at the home for three and a half years.
4 b Some animals, whose owners have mistreated them, look as if they have been through the mill.
5 e To animals that/which need new homes, an affectionate stroke suggests new hope.

Vocabulary animalcrackers
A *Words which sound different:*
dramatic, paramount, framework, paramedic

B 1 paramedic 2 dramatic 3 paramount
4 framework 5 hologram 6 cramp
7 gramophone 8 rampage 9 pram
10 ramble

Vocabulary Time expressions
A 1 a bit pressed for time 2 in time
3 at the best of times 4 buy time

Appearance and character
A 1b 2a 3c

B 1 The Minister doesn't come across well on TV.

2 The candidate I interviewed didn't seem (very) ambitious. / to have much ambition.
3 Pamela gave the impression of being rather insincere.
4 The last candidate struck me as being rather inexperienced.
5 Some of Peter's expressions remind me of my brother.
6 You have obviously made a big impression on Charlotte.

Reading and Summary
B 1A 2C 3A 4A 5A

C 1 the problem of having to absorb too much information
2 not stopping or talking / keeping our faces expressionless and looking straight ahead
3 our quick judgements about situations and people
4 the people we pass on the way to work
5 stereotypes
6 using dress and other visual clues to form a stereotype which demonstrates clearly what kind of person we are
7 the need to express our identity and create an opportunity for interaction with others
8 giving out information about fashion and price – thus signalling what kind of people we would like to make contact with

D *Points to include:*
1 We avoid and enable others to avoid taking in too much surrounding detail but we often ignore the plight of others.
2 We can make quick assumptions about people and situations which can have both useful and dangerous consequences.
3 We narrow our experience by depriving ourselves of things we might enjoy but can restrict contacts to groups we consider similar to ourselves and feel comfortable with.

Structure Rewriting
1 Agnes found some of her husband's religious views upsetting.
2 Who does that car belong to?
3 I was going to leave today, but I had to stay because of work.
4 The new Mercedes has been on sale since December.
5 Oh, just go away! You're being very annoying.
6 I don't / shouldn't imagine you will have any trouble getting a visa. / I imagine you will have no trouble getting a visa.
7 The house has been under (police) surveillance (by the police) for several weeks.
8 I do not regard the Prime Minister as (being) an exceptional leader.
9 The new terminal that / which is under construction will be finished next year.
10 It appears that poverty and crime are linked.

Vocabulary review

1C 2B 3C 4A 5A 6C 7D 8B 9B 10D

Cloze

1 such 2 with 3 ahead 4 carries / builds
5 where / when 6 longer 7 without
8 make 9 threat / use 10 theory
11 majority 12 being 13 according
14 whether 15 few / women / ones
16 whose 17 those 18 character
19 attempt 20 on

Vocabulary animalcrackers

A 1 feel 2 heel 3 reel 4 keel 5 peel

B The second e could become a in the syllable eel without causing a change in pronunciation, as in the word peal.

UNIT 3

Reading and Summary

B 1C 2C 3A 4C 5A 6D

D *Suggested answers*

1 causing anxiety 2 gruesome / weird
3 crumbling / falling to pieces
4 unfavourable / undesirable
5 darkest / dirtiest 6 hesitantly
7 with great concentration
8 great happiness, excitement or pride

E *Suggested answers*

1 have come in for a lot of criticism
2 like the innocuous sport mentioned, not something which would cause a lot of discussion or argument
3 it's not weapons but silver trophies which are displayed
4 when the gun is fired it jerks backwards in a violent way
5 we finish doing the activity
6 the idea of someone being prepared to shoot indiscriminately, which we are more familiar with than we should be

F *Points to include:*
Before
1 he hated violence
2 was certain he would hate the club
3 had preconceived notions about anyone involved with shooting
4 did not want to fire a weapon at all
After
5 surprised by the effect firing has
6 enjoyed it when he hit the target
7 still wary of the philosophy of being allowed to carry firearms
8 prepared to accept that different attitudes may have some justification

Vocabulary Related word groups

1 hl stare 2 fk glimpse 3 bo wink
4 am glance 5 cn peep 6 gi peer
7 dp blink 8 ej gaze

Structure

Rewriting: expressions with *do*

1 I'm fed up with always having to do / doing the donkey work.
2 Being poor never did anyone any good.
3 My brother (kindly) did me a favour (by) lending me his car for the weekend.

4 That new hairstyle does wonders for her.
5 Doing (up) this room (up) has really improved it.
6 Doctors say that smoking does you harm.
7 Richard lays / can lay carpets with his eyes closed now.
8 I couldn't have written the book without your help. / Without your help I couldn't have written the book.
9 The thief did time (in prison) for the crimes he had committed.
10 Teachers think that hard work does you no harm.

Cloze

1 off 2 more 3 according 4 likely
5 fact 6 times 7 had 8 when/while
9 however/though 10 from 11 at 12 on
13 being 14 raised 15 point/use 16 in
17 more 18 only 19 situation 20 reason

Vocabulary

Expressions to do with the weather

1 c get wind of 2 h bright and breezy
3 b an ill wind 4 d the calm before
5 f in a teacup 6 g make
7 e under 8 a weather

Blank-filling: Uses of *have* and *got*
Suggested answers

1 had / got my car serviced
2 had the police / anyone
3 won't have anyone / anybody 4 will have
5 had my car 6 got my neighbour's son
7 had / got my hair 8 to get

Vocabulary animalcrackers
Suggested answers

1 bull's-eye: the middle of the target
2 ebullient: full of energy and excitement
3 bulletin: short, official statement of news
4 bully: someone who frightens or hurts weaker people
5 bullet: missile fired from a gun
6 bullion: gold or silver in large amounts
7 bulldoze: force somebody to do something; level with a bulldozer
8 bullfinch: small bird with a pink breast

UNIT 4

Vocabulary

1 psychic 2 fortune 3 horoscope
4 premonition 5 clairvoyant 6 palmist
7 occult 8 telepathic 9 optical
10 medium 11 ghost 12 séance
Missing word: **superstition**

Cloze

1 towards 2 because 3 similarities
4 exist 5 claimed 6 could / would 7 into
8 got 9 place 10 nothing 11 hoax
12 far 13 as 14 must 15 refusal 16 of
17 based 18 carried 19 in
20 absence / lack

Reading and Summary

A 2 The Dream Detective

B 1B 2C 3A 4C 5D 6D

C 1 On 2 without 3 In spite of
4 between 5 by 6 Apart from

D *Points to include:*

1 The authorities were sceptical about his authenticity and regarded him with suspicion at first.
2 He was considered a fake by people who knew he could listen in to other people's phone calls.
3 Hearne is convinced that Robinson does posses psychic powers but feels he places too much emphasis on success and not enough on failure.
4 Official services are happy to make use of his powers but they do so clandestinely.

Structure Rewriting

1 John might not have been feeling well.
2 Mary could have become a concert pianist, but she didn't really want to.
3 You might have told me / I (really) wish you had told me that you had changed your plans.
4 I should not have spoken to her like that.
5 You could have killed yourself by touching that wire.
6 (It turned out that) I needn't have worried about my cat.
7 He must have followed you home, or he wouldn't know where you live.
8 I was supposed to pick / to have picked up Jane from the station, but I completely forgot about it.

Reading

B 1B 2E 3A 4C 5F 6D

C *Suggested answers*

1 Being mentally ill does not mean that you are wicked.
2 Serotonin is the chief subject of research in the area at present.
3 Normal levels regulate and control impulsive behaviour, e.g. aggression.
4 antisocial behaviour
5 We now know a great deal more about what different parts of the brain do, as a result of recent research.
6 The results are staggering because the proportion of persistent offenders who were found to have brain damage was so high – 90 per cent.
7 If so much crime springs from biological / chemical causes, we will have to rethink such moral questions as whether we should punish criminals or just provide medical treatment.

Vocabulary review

1C 2D 3B 4D 5B 6B 7D 8D

Structure Blank filling:
Chance and probabilities

1 is a foregone
2 doubt (very much) / very much doubt
3 In all
4 wouldn't have / never / would never have
5 bound / certain / sure to pass
6 unlikely / not likely

Vocabulary animalcrackers

A *Words which are pronounced or stressed differently:*
rebate, bathrobe, batch, probation, probate

B **a** batch **b** bathrobe **c** sabbatical
d combat **e** probate **f** rebate
g probation **h** battery

C **1** battery **2** rebate **3** probate **4** batch
5 sabbatical **6** bathrobe **7** probation
8 combat

Reading and Summary

A c

B 1D 2C 3A 4B 5D 6B

C *Suggested answers*
1 people addicted to travel
2 shocking shiny monsters
3 advanced laboriously feeling rather depressed
4 in the dreadfully high temperatures
5 observing miserably
6 the identical illogical scorn
7 indicated in a somewhat superior manner
8 to a switch which didn't look important
9 you rarely come across traffic jams
10 as if shocked by your audacity in passing them

D *Points to include:*
1 the 220 mile journey to the campsite in the intense heat
2 the fact that they could not get the air-conditioning to work
3 the aggressive behaviour of the juggernaut drivers
4 the fact that motor homes are not very easy to drive
Possible connecting words: in addition to (this fact), moreover, besides, furthermore

E 1 overtake 2 trudge 3 struggle
4 stagger 5 lumber 6 labour
7 plough 8 descend

Words used in a negative sense:
2, 3, 4, 5, 6, 7

Matching: 1f 2g 3b 4e 5h 6a 7c 8d

Connected with driving: overtake

Vocabulary Prefixes and suffixes

A uncomfortable, discomfort, dishonest, ignoble, unadventurous, inability/disability, unambitious, unlikely, mismanage, uninteresting

B worthless, pointless, hopeful/less, youthful, stressful, resentful

Vocabulary animalcrackers

1 triumphant 2 gigantic 3 frantic
4 significant 5 avant-garde 6 romantic
7 rampant 8 enchanting

Structure Transformations

1 I wish we had left for the airport earlier. / hadn't left for the airport so late.
2 If only we had rented a smaller motor home!

3 John regrets not checking / not having checked the departure times.
4 I wish you would stop / wouldn't keep (on) complaining about the heat!
5 We regret to inform you that your tickets have been mislaid.
6 I wish it didn't (always) take so long to fill in travel insurance documents.
7 I wish you wouldn't tell me / would stop telling me what to do.
8 I wish travelling weren't / wasn't so exhausting / were / was less exhausting.

Blank-filling

Suggested answers
1 to look on the bright
2 to look down their
3 he / the car had run out of
4 caught the thief
5 looked like drowned
6 were looking forward
7 arrived at their destination safe
8 the worse

Cloze Revision

dismal – miserable
a haven – a place of safety
on a whim – without careful consideration
chilling – frightening
nodding off – falling asleep
ostensibly – apparently
onset – beginning
unravelling – solving
get wind of – learn about / discover

Cloze Cloze development

The most famous British polar explorer –1– Captain Scott (1868–1912), a naval officer who led two expeditions to the Antarctic. The first expedition left England in August 1901 aboard the *Discovery*, a specially built wooden –2– . Scott's companions were Shackleton, who himself became famous as –3– Antarctic explorer, and the doctor, naturalist and artist Edward Wilson. They discovered the great ice-cap surrounding –4– South Pole and reached a point further south –5– anyone before them. Then, with their food running –6– and the dogs that pulled their sledge exhausted, they turned and struggled back. Scott –7– preparations for another Antarctic journey. The second expedition sailed in the whaling ship *Terra Nova*, and set –8– a large base ashore on Ross Island in 1911. Before the winter, the expedition laid out 'depots', or piles –9– food and fuel –10– the way towards the Pole. The polar journey began on November 1. The expedition had motor sledges and ponies as well –11– dogs for hauling the ordinary sledges, but the motors broke down after –12– few days. The decision to –13– ponies rather than dogs to pull the sledges on the final stages of the journey was –14– prove fatal. The expedition was unlucky –15– the weather and was delayed –16– very low temperatures and blizzards. The supporting party turned back leaving Scott to –17– out pulling a sledge with four companions. Towards the end of their ordeal, their food

and fuel exhausted, Scott wrote: 'for –18– own sake, I, myself, –19– not regret this journey'. In the following spring a search party from the base managed to –20– their bodies. They also recovered Scott's letters and diaries. The heroic end aroused the admiration of world.

1 was 2 ship 3 an 4 the 5 than
6 out 7 made 8 up 9 of 10 on /along
11 as 12 a 13 use 14 to 15 with
16 by 17 set 18 my 19 do
20 find / locate / retrieve

Cloze

A 1 It is valuable in that it is of symbolic importance to the Scottish people.
2 It has little commercial value or artistic merit.
3 They used it during coronations and other ceremonial events.
4 Because the circumstances under which it was acquired are not always clear-cut.
5 They are vast.
6 Anything of supreme cultural significance, or anything stolen.

B 1 have / get 2 more 3 value
4 significance / importance 5 being
6 to 7 occasions
8 rightful / true / original 9 source
10 what 11 circumstances
12 acquired / obtained 13 from / less
14 right 15 longer 16 probability
17 yet 18 strike 19 chances
20 without

Reading and Summary

A d a nun (The writer is Sister Wendy Beckett, a nun and well-known TV art critic.)

B 1A 2C 3A 4C 5B

C 1B 2C 3A 4B 5C

D *Points to include:*
Original motivation
1 It was originally intended to be a 'big journey' during which young men from 'good' families could learn about their own cultural beginnings.
2 The young men would then apply this knowledge in their future careers.
3 A learned companion would give the young men instruction to ensure that the learning process was effective.

Writer's motivation
1 No really great desire to trace her origins or see the world.
2 Agreed to go because she realized people were interested in what she had to say about art.
3 She wanted to be a 'human magnifying glass' for people to see through and perhaps encourage more people to have 'Grand Tours' in the future.
4 She wanted to tell people that artists can open up our view of reality.

Structure Rewriting

1 Her career / She changed tack when she was 30.
2 Maria is half French on her mother's side. / Maria is French only on her mother's side.
3 Janet's husband has an aggressive streak.
4 The film star is staying in a purpose-built caravan.
5 The delay meant that we missed our connecting flight.
6 The painter experimented with a lot of different techniques.
7 You must complete and return this form within 30 days.
8 A number of younger artists see (the) value in old customs and traditions.

Vocabulary
Gradable and ungradable adjectives
A 1C 2A 3B 4D 5B 6D 7C 8C 9D
10D 11D 12A 13B 14D 15A

Vocabulary animalcrackers
A 1 sc 2 h 3 gr 4 pr 5 b
bowl is pronounced differently from the others.

B *Suggested answers*
a prowling stealthily b howled dolefully
c scowled angrily d bowled rapidly
e growled angrily

Vocabulary review
1C 2C 3B 4C 5D 6A 7B 8B 9D
10C 11A 12B 13D 14D 15D

UNIT 7

Reading and Summary
A The photograph was taken in North America, in 1909. It shows a family of homesteaders travelling west.

C 1C 2B 3B 4B 5D 6C 7A

D 1 It built the rudiments of new cities, quickly and carelessly.
2 dependent on the railroad for all their needs
3 it had to be made 'visible' in words and pictures
4 The pamphlets tempted the reader with
5 freely available, lacking only people to claim them
6 a series of years with plenty of rain

E *Points to include:*
1 Photographs of up-and-coming cities showed
a a prosperous-looking community which was, in fact, bogus.
b railroad workers posing as citizens.
2 Writers and illustrators promised
a rich land waiting to be claimed.
b a new and improved lifestyle.
3 The government Act of 1909 increased the size of the land plots being given to settlers.

Structure Transformations

1 The perishable cargo had to be loaded quickly.
2 Popular literature was apparently distributed / appears to have been distributed throughout the US and Europe by railroad agents.
3 The settlers were led (, by the literature,) to believe that rich pickings awaited them.
4 Some homesteaders were thought to have already settled in Montana.
5 A large, free plot of land was promised to new settlers by/in the 1909 Act.
6 The semi-arid land was hastily disposed of by the government.
7 Westerners are said never to have recovered from this betrayal.
8 The temperature is said to have dropped to –40°C in 1916.

Rewriting

1 I can't help offending people, however much I try not to!
2 The venture has been a disaster but it can't be helped now.
3 Help yourself to a sandwich.
4 Let me help you out with all this paperwork.
5 The staff are always willing to lend a helping hand to customers in this store.
6 We are (running) short of coffee.

Blank-filling

1 did their / tried their
2 be taken down a peg or
3 amiss / the wrong way 4 short-comings
5 short-changed by 6 for the 7 take pot
8 is frowned

Vocabulary
1C 2A 3B 4C 5A 6B 7C 8B 9B
10C

Vocabulary animalcrackers
A Column 1 congratulate, fraternize
Column 2 migrate, infiltrate, generate, reiterate, perpetrate, concentrate
Column 3 rationalize
Column 4 ingratiate

B 1 ingratiate 2 fraternize
3 infiltrate 4 rationalize 5 perpetrate
6 congratulate 7 reiterate 8 migrate
9 concentrate 10 generate

Cloze
1 result(s) 2 for 3 likely 4 far 5 into
6 was/were 7 that 8 only 9 did
10 similar 11 through 12 of 13 least
14 in 15 would 16 may / might / could
17 much 18 came 19 themselves
20 having

UNIT 8

Cloze
B 1 refers 2 over 3 It 4 act
5 analysis / examination
6 reveal / give / provide
7 whether / if 8 where / when
9 scope / potential 10 such 11 lend

12 in 13 fortunes / futures 14 basis
15 towards 16 without 17 themselves
18 public 19 end 20 now

Structure Transformations
1 I'm worried about Jason because all he does is watch TV (all day).
2 What I can't understand is why you want to live in Africa at all.
3 It was Picasso who painted *Guernica*, not Dali.
4 It was because she saw Peter / seeing Peter with another woman that Harriet was upset. / that upset Harriet.
5 All I did was (to) turn it on.
6 It was only when the body was found that the police believed her.
7 so what he did was (to) break the window.
8 It was in 1914 that the First World War began.

Vocabulary Making opposites
B 1 incessant 2 implausible 3 incoherent
4 irreverent 5 illogical 6 immutable
7 inappropriate 8 indelible

C 1 illegal 2 impartial 3 illiterate
4 incorrect 5 irrational 6 irrelevant
7 insensitive / inconsiderate 8 immortal

Reading and Summary
B 1B 2D 3A 4B 5B

C *Points to include:*
Grandfather's fears
1 being surrounded by hidden people spying on them
2 being imprisoned in a dark place and tortured
3 only being able to see his granddaughter from the inside of a prison

Granddaughter's fears
1 being parted from her grandfather
2 being pursued and in danger for ever

Vocabulary Idioms
A 1 skeleton key
2 to pull the wool over someone's eyes
3 to throw the book at someone
4 mother tongue
5 to look like a drowned rat
6 to look down your nose
7 to catch someone's eye
8 to turn over a new leaf

B a skeleton key
b looked like a drowned rat
c mother tongue
d turn over a new leaf
e pull the wool over your eyes
f to catch her / his eye
g looks down her nose
h throw the book at you

C 1 to have memorized exactly
2 to deduce hidden meaning
3 to assume something
4 to be shocked into silence
5 verbatim

Vocabulary review
1C 2D 3A 4C 5C 6D 7B 8C 9C
10B 11A 12D 13D 14A 15B

Vocabulary animalcrackers

A 1 an early bird 2 a busy bee
3 a lone wolf 4 a sitting duck
5 a cold fish 6 a bookworm
7 a dark horse 8 a snail's pace

UNIT 9

Writing   Metamorphosis

A 1 *Frogspawn*
   feeding on yolks inside jelly
   hatching
2 *Tadpole*
   breathing through gills
   gulping air from the surface of the
     water
   developing lungs;
   swimming with the aid of a long tail
   forming limbs
3 *Adult frog*
   leaving the water
   losing their long tail
   climbing trees
   hopping
   breeding
   hibernating in winter in northern
     countries

Reading

A *The following information should be
included in answers:*
1 Convincing the local population of the
   importance of preserving wildlife.
2 Natural habitats of wild animals have
   been turned into farmland which, in
   turn, has led to a ruined environment, a
   lowering of social standards, a poor
   standard of living, and not enough food.
3 To raise both money for and awareness
   of the struggle between local people and
   wildlife.
4 People who have learned to come to
   terms with the difficult conditions in
   which they live.
5 Some were fascinated by the strange
   spectacle, others were somewhat afraid
   but were enthusiastic about the visit.

B 1 turning wild habitats into farmland
2 the support of the local people
3 the fact that previous attempts at
   conservation have not taken into
   consideration the support of the local
   people
4 the edge of the national park
5 people who live in close contact with
   wildlife
6 the buffalo and the elephant

C 1 resistance 2 assured 3 consolation
4 adopting 5 effects 6 specimens
7 degeneration 8 habitats

Structure   Blank-filling

1 havoc 2 it by ear 3 foul
4 the verge / point / brink
5 grateful if you could / would 6 a duck to
7 water off a duck's 8 fish in a small
9 ban on the 10 hadn't made

Transformations

1 Should there be an emergency / an
   emergency arise, break the glass and sound
   the alarm.
2 If I were to get the job abroad, would you
   come with me?
3 Had the livestock been brought in for the
   night, many (of the) animals would not
   have perished.
4 Unless we take steps / steps are taken to
   preserve natural resources, the planet will
   be in danger.
5 If only we hadn't booked that camping
   holiday!
6 If the government were considering raising
   taxes immediately, they would never have
   just lowered them.
7 Were it not for the fact that Sally is very
   disorganized, she might / would have a
   chance of getting that secretarial job.
8 If it hadn't been for the fact that the road
   was water-logged, we would / might have
   been able to move our vehicle.

Cloze and Summary
Cloze development

A 1 Unlike 2 lonely 3 sights 4 rising
5 arrived 6 another 7 although
8 stage 9 whatever 10 as 11 every
12 celebrated 13 over / during / in
14 if 15 lose 16 survival

B *Points to include:*
Hitherto local people have been hostile to
the idea of wildlife conservation as wildlife
prevents them from farming successfully.
They have failed to see any personal
benefits from local wildlife and so have
been unable to identify with efforts to
conserve it. However, far from being bitter
and apathetic, villagers have fought
valiantly to come to terms with the wildlife
on their doorsteps and they hold the
wildlife in respect.

Vocabulary   animalcrackers

ae scattered, categorical, catastrophic,
    cataclysmic, catty, catalogued
ei located, vocational, desiccated
ə delicate, catastrophe

1 located 2 scattered 3 catty
4 categorical 5 vocational 6 delicate
7 desiccated 8 cataclysmic, catastrophic
9 catalogued 10 catastrophe

Vocabulary   Lost consonants

A 1 spending 2 firm 3 part 4 hang
5 kind 6 start 7 first 8 completed

Writing   Project tiger
Suggested answers
Habits
Tigers like to swim...
Tigers are excellent swimmers.
Most cats do not like to swim.
Tigers rest for most of the day.
Tigers usually start hunting late in the
afternoon.
They prefer to hunt by ambushing passing
animals.

Their striped coats give the perfect
   camouflage ...
They usually hunt alone.
They occasionally hunt as a pair.
An adult tiger will eat 18–27 kg of meat at
   one feed.
Endangered species
Tigers are an endangered species.
There are fewer than 6,000 tigers in the wild.
The main threat today comes from poachers.
They kill tigers for their bones.
Tigers' bones are used in traditional Chinese
   medicine.
The other danger comes from the destruction
   of the forests.
The forests are being destroyed by the human
   population.
The human population need to use the
   forests for agriculture.
Tigers depend on forests for their survival.
They are unable to hunt in open country.
They have very little endurance.
The destruction of tiger habitats may
   continue.
Tigers may become extinct.

UNIT 10

Cloze

1 rather 2 any 3 According 4 success
5 what 6 all 7 doing 8 leads 9 cause
10 it 11 for 12 applies 13 however
14 going 15 so
16 Secondly / Next / Then
17 Finally / Thirdly / Last(ly) 18 reached
19 solved / resolved 20 preferable

Vocabulary   animalcrackers

A 1 apex 2 aperture 3 agape 4 aperitif
5 drape 6 cape

B In 1, 2, and 4 the letters *ape* are pronounced
differently.

Reading and Summary

A 1T 2F 3T 4T 5F

B 1B 2A 3B 4A 5C 6C

C 1A 2A 3D 4C 5A 6C 7A 8A 9B
10B

D *Points to include:*
1 He was given a tutor but he never
   learned to speak.
2 He was looked after by a loving helper
   but never loved in return.
3 He was invited to dinner, stole some
   small items, then he hid up a tree.
4 The tutor let the boy think he no longer
   cared for him and the boy learned how
   cruel people can be and was upset.
5 Despite trying to help him fit into a
   civilized society the boy never related to
   anyone but himself.

Structure   Tense and context

2g 3b 4h 5d 6f 7l 8a 9e 10c 11k 12i

Tense review

1 has been improving 2 has changed
3 it had been snowing 4 has been working
5 will have been digging

6 have you been going out
7 had been killed 8 have been meaning
9 will have finished 10 had been broken

Rewriting
1 There has been a significant deterioration in his father's condition.
2 After the crash, the runway was littered with debris.
3 I spent ages waiting for a bus to arrive.
4 The Minister took full responsibility for what had gone wrong.
5 My mother had misgivings about my decision to become an actor.
6 I drove 200 miles to the concert, only to find that I had gone on the wrong day.
7 Would you like to make a contribution to our campaign?
8 I've got to cut down on chocolate as part of my diet.

Vocabulary review
1C 2C 3B 4A 5D 6D 7C 8C 9D
10B 11A 12B 13C 14C 15D

Writing   Varieties of English
I went to the theatre last Thursday with Jane's brother, and we saw King Lear at Stratford. Unfortunately Jane couldn't come with us because she works *from Monday to Friday,* and it means she's only free *at the weekend(s)*. Anyway it was great, although while we were driving back we ran out of *petrol* and had to be rescued by a *policeman,* and by the time *we got back* to Jane's flat it was nearly three in the morning! Jane was *really angry* with her brother when she heard about it and said it was the *most stupid* thing she'd ever heard of.

Well, I'd better go now. Jane *has* just got back and we're going out for a drink with her *mother / mum*. I'll *ring* you on Friday – I hope you don't mind if I make a *transfer charge* call.

Hope everything's OK with you, and don't forget to write *to* me soon.

UNIT 11

Reading and Summary
B 1C 2A 3D 4C 5B 6C

C 1A 2B 3C 4C 5A 6C 7B 8A 9C
10A 11B 12A

D *Suggested answers*
1 excursion; stumble
2 fight with fists; square on a form to tick
3 happy 4 uses a keyboard
5 aesthetic sense 6 move recklessly
7 sent on an assignment; put on a notice board
8 reckless 9 gifts
10 exact / precise; a lead weight

E *Punctuation*
Check answers in the text on p56.

Reported speech
1 Cheskin admitted that he had found it difficult to believe the results after the first 200 interviews. He confessed, however, that after 1,000 interviews he had had to accept the fact that the majority of consumers transferred the sensation from the container to its contents.
2 Stan Gross, a marketing consultant in Pennsylvania, commented that he couldn't ask people why they liked a certain package, and they couldn't tell him. He added that the package was not silent. It screamed – but it screamed to people's inner mind.
3 Gross asks people to write the obituary of a toothpaste, if it were a person, or he asks them what a film would be about if it were a detergent.
4 Gross says that buying things is a way of coping.

F *Points to include:*
1 Packaging sends loud messages to our subconscious mind.
2 It is possible to find out what people really think by involving them in seemingly childish activities like playing games.
3 Although consumers know the purchases they make will not provide them with what they are looking for, buying them helps them to live their lives and deal with their problems.
4 The attractive displays competing against each other also give consumers satisfaction.

Structure   Transformations
1 The security guard denied that he (had) had / having had anything whatsoever to do with the theft.
2 The Marketing Manager suggested trying to buy / suggested (that) they should try to buy more products in bulk.
3 The Sales Manager warned that unless the firm improved its sales figures, it would go to the wall.
4 The foreman boasted that Zenco was the best packaging company in the country.
5 The accountant conceded that the company was only just managing to break even.
6 The consultant insisted (to the board) that he had taken all aspects of the company's performance into consideration.
7 The factory owner announced to the workers (that) that day was a day which would go down in history.
8 The reporter accused the government of consistently failing / having consistently failed to support small businesses.

Rewriting
Suggested answers
1 The company went to the wall because of a sudden price rise in raw materials. / The fact that the company went to the wall was due to a sudden price rise in raw materials. / A sudden price rise in raw materials caused the company to go to the wall.
2 Peter urged his son not to make any decisions yet.
3 There is no call for products which seem to lack credibility.
4 Many people find themselves in (financial) difficulties by purchasing / buying goods on credit.
5 John Samson dabbled in buying old maps.
6 Susan suggested that William should invest / invested some of the money he had inherited.
7 The twins are always picking arguments with / picking on each other.
8 We have no small sizes in stock. / We are out of stock of small sizes. / Small sizes are out of stock.

Cloze   Cloze development
A The 28-year-old had spent six years working nights –1 **while**– she gained her university degree during the day. 'I always wanted –2 **to**– be a teacher,' she said, 'and I worked hard to earn my degree. When I –3 **finally**– graduated, I was very optimistic.' She had her eye –4 **on**– a teaching position at a nearby primary school. With the help of friends who teach at –5 **the**– school, she landed an interview with the Head. 'I noticed a tiny ladder in my tights earlier,' she recalls. 'I thought –6 **about**– changing them, but I knew I'd be late if I did. And –7 **by**– the time I got to the interview, it was enormous. I walked in apologizing –8 **for**– not looking my best.' The would-be teacher didn't get the job. In fact one of her friends told –9 **her**– that the Head's only comment was: 'If someone doesn't take the time to present her best image at –10 **an**– interview, what kind of teacher is she going to be?' First impressions are lasting ones. Indeed, –11 **if**– you play your cards right, you can enjoy the benefits of what sociologists –12 **call**– the 'halo effect'. This means that if you're viewed positively within the critical first –13 **four**– minutes, the person you've met will probably assume –14 **everything**– you do is positive. Bungle a first encounter, and often the interviewer will assume you have a host of –15 **other**– negative traits. Worse, he or she may not take the time to give –16 **you**– a second chance. Most employers believe that those who look as if they care about themselves will care –17 **more**– about their jobs. So aim to come –18 **across**– in the best possible light – attractive in the way you dress, in your gestures, facial expressions and in your speech. We know it's what's –19 **inside**– that counts, but research shows that personable people are generally perceived –20 **as**– more intelligent, likeable and credible.

B She said she had always wanted to be a teacher, and she had worked hard to earn her degree. When she had finally graduated, she had been very optimistic. She recalled that she had noticed a tiny ladder in her tights earlier that day. She said she had thought about changing them, but she had known / knew she would have been / be late if she had. By the time she (had) got to the interview, it was enormous. She had walked in apologizing for not looking her best. The Head had later commented to one of her friends that if someone didn't take the time to present her best image at an interview, it was difficult to know what kind of teacher she was going to be. / she was unlikely to be a good teacher.

Vocabulary animalcrackers

A No change in pronunciation.

B 1 lapdog 2 dog-eared
3 in the doghouse 4 dogmatic
5 doggie paddle 6 dogging
7 dogsbody 8 lie doggo

C 1 dogmatic 2 doggie paddle
3 dogsbody 4 lapdog
5 dogged 6 in the doghouse
7 dog-eared 8 lying doggo

UNIT 12

Vocabulary Crime

1 shoplifting 2 sentenced 3 arson
4 reckless 5 fraud 6 assault 7 witness
8 punishments 9 convicted 10 libel
11 trial 12 evasion 13 verdict
Missing name: **Hercule Poirot**

Structure *Use, to use, used to, used to doing, useless*

A 1 am used to 2 used to 3 used to
4 use 5 is no use / is useless 6 use
7 use 8 use 9 used to
10 is no use / is useless

Reading

B 1A 2A 3C 4B 5C

C 1c 2d 3b 4f 5a 6h 7e 8g

1 late 2 junior 3 mugging(s) 4 wheeze
5 affronted 6 doggedly 7 coincidence
8 tremulously

Structure
Rewriting: Gerunds and infinitives
Suggested answers

1 He returned home to find that his flat had been ransacked.
2 If you want to catch the 5.15 train, it will mean having to leave early. / leaving early.
3 I really regret saying / having said what I did.
4 There is no point (in) trying to make me change my mind.
5 The manager (said he) was unwilling to lend me what I needed.
6 The Prime Minister has no intention of resigning.
7 Mozart died without finishing his last work.
8 Jack was one of the first (people) to be / get promoted.
9 It came as a great surprise to Emma to hear / when she heard that she had passed the exam.
10 I'll never forget seeing the Pyramids for the first time.

Cloze

1 appeals 2 to 3 met / supplied 4 used
5 in 6 tend 7 over 8 version 9 that
10 add / introduce 11 words 12 out
13 way 14 theme 15 where 16 end
17 first / most 18 prior 19 It 20 deal

Vocabulary review

1B 2B 3A 4A 5C 6D 7C 8D 9B 10B

Vocabulary animalcrackers

A *apprehend* – seize or arrest
comprehend – understand
reprehend – blame or find fault with

The letters *hen* are pronounced differently in *phenomenon*.

UNIT 13

Reading and Summary

B 1C 2D 3D 4D 5A 6C

C *Suggested answers*

1 wearing very little indeed
2 a sudden and spectacular fall out of favour
3 discovered that it was no longer approved of
4 to attract most normal, conventional people
5 making all other travelling circuses look small
6 to entice people to attend circus performances once again
7 the last part of the puzzle
8 people who a) throw several things up in the air at once and catch them and b) are skilled at bending and twisting their bodies to entertain others

D *Points to include:*
Reasons for the decline

1 increase in the costs of staging the show
2 very high taxes on entertainment
3 lack of public interest
4 adverse publicity about cruelty to animals
5 young people now favouring video and computer games

Measures taken by Gandey

1 creation of a new, original circus
2 hiring of exciting, international, speciality acts
3 no animals to be used
4 specially commissioned rock music performed by a renowned musician
5 introduction of acts to astound audiences

Vocabulary review

A 1C 2C 3D 4C 5D 6A 7B 8C

B origin; originate / creation; creative / persuasion; persuade / competition; competitive / unfashionable / indifference / publicize; public / progress; progressive / prohibition; prohibit / enthusiasm; enthuse

Structure Rewriting

1 The company will have to make the best of a bad job.
2 The company failed to find a suitable play to draw audiences back to the theatre.
3 The director is always making / always makes a mountain out of a molehill.
4 It suddenly dawned on me why the audience was being so hostile.
5 No sooner had the concert ended than there was a loud scream from backstage.
6 Little did the actors realize that the scenery was about to fall on them.
7 Rock musician Rick Wakeman made his name in the 1970s.
8 Only by practising day after day did the performer learn how to juggle.
9 The *Cirque Surreal* exemplifies an out-of-this-world experience.
10 Entertainment cannot be popular without being sympathetic to the needs of its audience.

Blank-filling
Suggested answers

1 were they short of money
2 did he say / utter 3 survival / surviving
4 to be thought 5 to nothing
6 to the south / east / west lay
7 we arrived at the theatre / cinema
8 get the hang 9 decline 10 spread like

Positive or Negative?

Positive 1, 5, 7, 8, 9, 11
Negative 2, 3, 4, 6, 10, 12

Cloze

1 fame 2 since / subsequently
3 included 4 names 5 falling / going
6 fought 7 recent
8 regards / views / considers / sees
9 which 10 attracted / drawn / attached
11 would 12 part 13 decline 14 lost
15 So 16 speaking 17 end 18 find
19 way 20 own

Writing
Suggested reply

… thanks / would like to thank Phillip Gandey for his kind invitation to a Gala Opening of the Cirque Surreal on Saturday, 9th October at the Fortune Theatre, Main Street West at 7.30 / and has great pleasure in accepting. / but regrets that (s)he is unable to accept due to (a prior engagement).

Vocabulary animalcrackers

A flysheet flypaper flyaway flytip
flyleaf chiefly flyer briefly
flyover (possibly 'overfly') horsefly

chiefly and *briefly* are pronounced differently

B 1 chiefly 2 flysheet 3 flyleaf 4 flytip
5 flypaper 6 flyover 7 flyaway
8 briefly 9 flyer 10 horsefly

UNIT 14

Cloze

1 relied / depended 2 would
3 when 4 its
5 allowed / permitted / helped / enabled

6 be 7 not 8 that 9 contrary 10 fact
11 growth 12 that 13 solution
14 minimum 15 volcano 16 if
17 different 18 led 19 unaffected
20 edge(s)

Vocabulary review Expressions
1D 2C 3B 4B 5C 6C

Reading and Summary
B 1D 2B 3C 4A 5C

C 1a 2b 3f 4e 5c 6d

1 distress 2 admitted 3 labyrinthine
4 truncated 5 host 6 insatiable

D *Points to include:*
1 The Nagamas annoyed the writer with their constant begging for money and tugging at his clothes.
2 Nearly all the modern Egyptians – couples, families and groups of students – greeted the writer in a friendly way and many invited him to eat with them.
3 The tourist policeman tried to fine him fifteen Egyptian pounds but was happy to settle for one Egyptian pound.

Structure Forms of the future
1 will 2 am giving 3 won't start
4 am going to catch 5 Shall
6 am going to be 7 will be
8 are not to 9 will have looked up
10 I'll 11 were getting 12 was going to
13 will be getting rid of 14 will be

Vocabulary review
The environment
1C 2B 3D 4B 5A 6A 7C 8C

Vocabulary animalcrackers
A 1b 2e 3d 4c 5a

The letters *emu* are pronounced in the same way in the first and fifth words and the third and fourth words.

B 1 mercury – c, h, i
2 medium – b. e, f
3 mule – a, d, g

Writing Arguments
1 a It is often suggested that
b It could be argued that / Some people would argue that
2 a To a certain limited extent, there is some truth in this. However
b This is partly true, but / This argument has a certain superficial logic, but
3 a It is therefore quite wrong to suggest that...; on the contrary
b It is clear that / The real situation is that

Unit 15

Reading and Summary
A c

B 1d 2c 3e 4f 5b 6a

C 1 a lot of fuss about nothing
2 every little corner and place
3 to speak plainly
4 we've been fooled
5 idiots

---

6 Are we not being told about something?
7 a much more ambitious concept to accept

D 1B 2B 3D 4C

E *Points to include:*
Theory one: Both the media and the couple knew no wedding had been arranged but both pretended that it had for their own ends.
Theory two: The couple had gone to a lot of trouble to pretend they were going to get married to ensure that the new album by their rivals, *Blur,* would not obtain maximum publicity.
Theory three: Officially the couple had called the wedding off because of media intrusion into their privacy.
Theory four: Nobody knows what really happened but the public had been tricked once again.
Theory five: The couple had married secretly after all.

Structure Grammatical errors
1 trying *making* light *to make* light
2 Nor *it was* *was it*
3 Mr Tipper *has* spent *spent*
4 *made* sure *to make* / *making* sure
5 had *froze* had frozen
6 problem / first problem *was* first noticed
7 *that* is hit *which* is hit
8 Mr Tipper *was spending* *spent*
9 hammers / that *so* that
10 I wish it *hasn't* been *hadn't* been
11 I'm not *using* to *used* to
12 absolutely *pleased* *delighted* / *thrilled*
13 no signs *to loosen* *of loosening*
14 *record-break* record-break*ing*

Cloze
1 in 2 after 3 who 4 on 5 to / towards
6 although / though 7 with 8 from
9 into 10 about 11 preventing 12 as

Vocabulary Expressions
1 book 2 blanket 3 knot 4 leaf
5 armchair 6 wind

Headlines
Head gets foot in door: literally a head and a foot as parts of the body; actual meaning 'Headteacher or head of a company, has a prospect of success.'
Police found safe under blanket: this can have an active meaning 'Police found a safe (strongbox) under a blanket', or a passive meaning 'some police officers were found safe (and well) under a blanket'.
Passengers hit by cancelled trains: *hit* can mean 'were hit' or were 'affected by'.
Skeleton staff in hospital: You might associate skeletons with hospital but a *skeleton staff* is the smallest number of staff needed to do a job.

Structure Blank-filling
Suggested answers
1 came up 2 to writing 3 only had it
4 must have 5 had (very) little/ no/ didn't have any 6 take it 7 matter how

---

8 read between the 9 be threatened / faced
10 to be thought

Transformations
1 Mrs Tipper greatly regretted not being able to celebrate the New Year with her husband.
2 Not only do the tabloids provide news but they (also) provide entertainment (as well).
3 It was only when they arrived at the venue that the journalists heard about the changes to the wedding plans.
4 The minister is under a cloud for / because of his involvement in that corruption scandal.
5 I wish I had been more patient with the children.
6 The band is thought to have split up many times before.
7 If the students had paid enough / more attention during the training session, they could / would be able to follow their instructions correctly.
8 If it hadn't been for the / such dreadful weather, the basketball match wouldn't have been cancelled.
9 By the time David arrived in the car park the supermarket had closed.
10 The more qualifications you are able to amass, the more success you will have in the academic field.
11 Susan insisted on driving Jim home.
12 Hardly had we finished dinner when Mrs Jones arrived on the doorstep.

Rewriting
1 Operating / The operation of this new machinery demands technical skills.
2 We decided to have a meal in the restaurant to kill time before the plane took off. / We had to wait ages for the plane to take off so we decided to kill time by having a meal in the restaurant.
3 Crimes of passion are as old as the hills.
4 This television programme bears a strong resemblance to one I saw last month.
5 The police caught the burglar red-handed. / The burglar was caught red-handed breaking the jeweller's window.
6 It seems Susan has changed her mind about going to university. / Susan seems to have changed her mind about going to university.
7 Tabloid sensationalism is frowned upon in this office.
8 Patsy and Liam seemed to be having second thoughts about marriage.
9 It suddenly dawned on Claire what a blunder she had made.
10 You must resign yourself to the fact that this part of your life has come to an end.

Vocabulary animalcrackers
1 goat 2 rat 3 horse 4 cat and mouse
5 fish 6 fish 7 snake 8 duck 9 fish
10 donkey